PRINCIF
OF
S ecurity
Surveying

by
GEORGE SCOTT

Published by:
Paramount Publishing Ltd.
Paramount House
17/21 Shenley Road
Borehamwood
Herts. WD6 1RT.
Tel: 01-207 5599
Telex: 944036 P MOUNT G

ISBN 0 947665 09 9

The Author

George Scott is the pseudonym of a
man who began his involvement with
the security industry in 1970, when
he changed his position within
Insurance from that of an underwriter
to that of surveying, having spent
some time before as a new business
inspector. His initial surveying career
was in the provinces, but for the last
14 years he has operated in the
Greater London area.

Whilst in the provinces he was a local
secretary of the Chartered Insurance
Institute and served also on their
Education Committee, and in London
he has been associated with ABIS
Ltd.

He has no false illusions about being
an academic, believing firmly that
more problems are solved by
experience and the application of
commonsense than by illusory
theory.

PRINCIPLES OF SECURITY SURVEYING

Contents

Page

Introduction

Over a period of several years I have read many publications, either books or articles in magazines, which are written with at least part of the intention being to help surveyors. The majority of these have been very good, although I did read one meant for the use of Architects and this was nothing short of disgraceful and in many instances downright wrong, and if the advice therein was heeded then there is going to be a lot of poor security in existence directly due to that writing. There was actually an illustration of a floor safe upside down, obviously an error, (or was it to be ceiling mounted?) but indicative of the general standard as that was by no means the only error.

One criticism, however, of those books or articles which are good, is that the vast majority are pitched at too high a level, thus leaving the inexperienced surveyor in a confused state, in that he is struggling to understand the advanced side of the business without having mastered the basics. There is very little for him to refer to in this basic connection and there is not always a colleague handy with the necessary free time to sit down and explain the problem concerned. I think that the difficulty is, and this is not intended as an insulting comment upon the expert, that many experienced and expert practitioners cannot get down to the level of the beginner when it comes to the art of communication. Not being an expert in any field whatsoever, I find that I am about to try and fill this gap. It will probably become all too apparent that I am not an expert in communication, but I will have a go anyway.

This book is not designed for the experienced surveyor to whom its contents will be mundane and second nature. It is intended to be used by the novice surveyor; anyone who has, in the course of his duties, to carry out some surveys or anyone who is expected to understand survey reports, yet has seldom, if ever, seen a survey carried out. The making of recommendations to improve security standards is, of course, implied with all these categories. The reader will find many references to "insurance" throughout this book. Even if the surveyor's client is not insured in the accepted sense, this merely means that he is prepared to carry his own risk in the form of self-insurance. Additionally, compliance with insurance security recommendations is often the reason a client calls in a consultant/surveyor so that knowledge of insurance thinking will always be an advantage.

Anyone who benefits from any part of this book is more than welcome.

In writing this book I must pay due thanks to those who have influenced me over the years and who have made my surveying career that bit more understandable and enjoyable. Whilst singling out individuals is probably quite incorrect that is exactly what I am going to do. There is an old (now retired) warhorse with whom I worked for several years, and who taught me more than anyone else about the art of being flexible without being weak. He is beloved by many, confusing to some and a pain in the anatomy to others, but I believe in taking people how you find them and not relying on other's opinions. I am, of course, referring to Jack Worsley who always reminded me to look for the basics, not to try and be smart for the sake of showing one's so-called ability, to remember the costs and always to be constructive and reasonable. Thank you Jack, and there's no cheque in the post!

One thing I must impress upon all readers — no book will solve all your problems, no book will prepare you for all that you are about to encounter and no book can "teach" you about surveying. All I can say is that, hopefully, this book will point you in the right direction and eliminate some of the more basic, and therefore embarrassing, errors.

Earlier I mentioned several groups who might benefit, but I cannot write with all of you in mind. This book is therefore written with the surveyor (of the novice variety) in mind. I ask the rest of you to try and put yourself in his shoes — it is not painful, I assure you.

I must, finally, pay sincere thanks to those kind, long suffering, people who have helped me enormously by editing, correcting and generally putting me right. Thank you Norman (,) Dunkerley, Alan (!) Tagg, Roy Reed and Colin Bridges.

CHAPTER 1

What is a Surveyor?

It seems reasonable to begin by considering the people involved, what they have to know and what they have to do.

The *"job description"* of a surveyor will vary in detail depending upon the employer, but in general terms he (she) is expected to assess a risk from a security aspect and report on the relevant facts, with any necessary suggestions for risk improvement.

To enable us to think of a surveyor's activities, we must first of all consider what he is up against. Security is not an exact science, nor, in my opinion, is it a subject suitable to be taken over by that master of all masters, the computer. The devising of security methods, standards, systems, call them what you like, is, in its most simplified form, a battle of wits, implying thought, and computers cannot think for themselves. The battle is between two sets of people with vastly differing (I hope) sets of principles, viz the law breaker and the law preserver. However, unlike other forms of combat, *e.g.* chess, tennis, soccer, etc., the surveyor does not know the strengths and weaknesses of his particular adversary. Burglars, like other people, have varying degrees of ability, interest, expertise, etc. Consequently, it is an unfair contest because, whilst the surveyor knows little about the burglar, the burglar can know a fair amount about the protected risk, he can see many of the items, bars, bolts, alarm components, etc., and has the opportunity to study the risk and plan his strategy, knowing what he is up against.

If security is an unfair contest you may well ask if there is really any point in trying to put it into practice? Often you will be faced with a client whose attitude is *"why bother, if they want to get in, they will, regardless of what you do to try and stop them."* Admittedly, as a surveyor, I am biased, but I certainly believe that the reasonable application of security devices and methods is most worthwhile. It must deter some criminals from entering premises, especially when there are a large number of other poorly protected premises to provide alternative targets. To go into the pros and cons of whether or not security is worthwhile is not the object of this book, but you can imagine the situation if no-one bothered; no-one and nowhere would be safe. Admittedly, when you read of the crimes of rape, mugging etc, you might be inclined to agree with that sentiment, but those crimes, horrendous as they are, are not in our direct field of concern as surveyors, though they most definitely are as private citizens. We are concerned basically with the breaking and entering of buildings or property resulting in illegal removal of people's possessions, or the destruction of same. We must, in this book, confine ourselves to that line or else the book would be quite enormous.

I believe that without reasonable standards of security the burglar would be in his form of heaven. Hopefully you are converted to that line of thought also. If, however, you are in any doubt you are most certainly in the wrong job and should get out before you do some damage to others.

As mentioned earlier, burglars come in all forms. Some members of the public still think they are all large bruisers with striped jerseys and masks, carrying bags with *"swag"* on their backs. The silent movies have a lot to answer for, so some of my older colleagues tell me.

Although we might not like to acknowledge the fact, we actually have something in common with the burglar. We are all members of the human race. So just as we, on the right side of the law, have individualistic traits and qualities, so do they. Just as we have both geniuses and bunglers, so do they. Unfortunately, the bungling burglar (try saying that quickly after a drink or six) can cause damage even if his haul is not large. He can also cause considerable heartache if his deeds are carried out in private houses.

If you look at the foot of the burglar expertise range you find the (comparatively) petty chappy who is quite content with the portable radio taken from the ledge of the open and inviting window. Go up a step and you get the more daring chappy who is going to enter the premises and still be content with a fairly small *"take"*, and so on up the scale to the bullion chappy at the top of the pile. In between these two extremes you will find a variety of degrees of ability, daring, bravery and all the other attributes that it takes to make a successful burglar. It is often said that bullies are only brave when they are in groups. Well some burglars will perform some amazing feats of courage and daring whether they are in a gang or on their own. They will scale heights that would put me into a cold sweat.

There is probably only one *"standard element"* in the burglar fraternity, ie the more daring or skilful the job requirements, the greater the returns they will expect to receive. Their skills come at a price, they may be illegal, but they are certainly not stupid. I have no doubt that some of you, like me, have read of a burglary which, when you assimilate the details, you find you end up with a sneaking respect for the burglars' cunning or craftiness, but of course you will not condone their actions, will you? One thing all burglars have in common is that they all run the risk of being caught and given a free holiday at yours and my expense. Whilst they might not fear the prison regime, they will be temporarily deprived of the ability to earn their ill gotten gains. Mind you, there is a school of thought that whilst on their enforced holiday they will learn more tricks of the trade and come out even better prepared to carry on their business.

I repeat my earlier assertion that even modest security is definitely necessary, otherwise it would be easier for the learner to earn his stripes at the burglary profession. I say easier because it is quite amazing how many premises exist without even rudimentary security, and as long as this situation continues to exist there will always be a training school for burglars.

The surveyor has to contend not only with the variety of burglar, the variety of premises and variety of goods, but also a great variety of clients with which to deal. They will vary in degree of intelligence (a fact, not an insult), degree of co-operation (many do not want security and only install it, begrudgingly, to obtain insurance cover), physical ability (not many elderly people, crippled with arthritis, are going to be able to use floor safes), and so on. In this multi-racial country of ours even the language can be a problem in simply trying to extract certain important facts, or trying to convey what you want the client to do.

I feel, sometimes, that the *"language problem"* exists as a matter of convenience, because some of those with this problem in understanding the language seem remarkably good at making a very good living from the residents of this land. However, when such suspicions arise it can be very difficult to prove, and if you can't prove it be very careful to whom you express your opinions or suspicions, or it could be you that ends up in trouble with the law!

The foregoing is by no means an exhaustive list of the possible snags, problems, and adversaries a surveyor may have to confront, only a sample, but, hopefully, sufficient to make the points that the job (a) cannot be computerised satisfactorily, and (b) is a good challenge to anyone who takes it on.

What, then of the surveyor himself. What are the attributes, attitudes and degrees of expertise required of him? To me, far and away the most important factor in a good surveyor's make-up is his attitude to his work and his clients. Let us take his work attitude first. He is not involved in crime prevention even though that may be a beneficial spin-off from his work. His job is loss prevention, or loss reduction, if we are to be more accurate. By making a set of premises reasonably secure he need not have prevented any crime at all, but he may well have moved that crime to other areas. It is argued that the increase in *"mugging"*, etc., is a result of greater security in premises, thus making *"the person"* an easier target than *"the premises"*, but that is not the subject of this book. Making premises *"burglar proof"* is not his job either, for two reasons: the first is that to do so is virtually impossible because of the cost factor. The only places likely to even approach that standard are nuclear or military establishments where costs are less important. The second reason is because to do so is self-defeating. Burglar proof premises will not require his services again. In its context, the surveyor's job is to ensure that the security of the premises involved is of a standard to prevent the majority of potential losses and thus make it a reasonable proposition for insurance (even if the client is not officially "insured", he will be carrying his own financial risk in respect of any theft). We will, for the moment at least, ignore the argument that every risk, regardless of its security *"has its price"* or that inferior security can be compensated by increased premiums, a theory with which I am in disagreement and will continue to be until someone practising this theory explains how they calculate the variables. I know for a fact that some Insurers operate this procedure, but, as I say, it must be on the crystal ball basis as there is no scientific way (as far as I have been able to find out) of knowing "the cost" of a good lock as against a lesser model, or of one standard of alarm as against another of lesser quality.

Assuming the correct attitude to the job in general, let us now turn to more particular job attitudes. Surveyors do, unfortunately, exist who are determined that *"there will be no losses on any of my cases"*. Whether this is a product of uncertainty or arrogance is open to doubt, but, in either case, they do surveyors in general no good at all. To fulfil this objective not only requires belt and braces but ties, string, safety pins and other bits and pieces, and you know how easy it is for the innocent to be tarred with the same brush as the guilty. Trying not to be *"belt and braces"* is not an open invitation to be careless or cavalier in attitude. The surveyor has, having assessed the risk, to be firm, but don't confuse firmness with dogmatism. He must be prepared to listen to reasonable arguments and possibly accept alternatives to his own specification without necessarily weakening the end result. To take this a stage further, after reasoned discussion a surveyor should not be afraid to admit he is wrong; as far as I am aware no-one from managing director down is infallible. We can all make mistakes, but don't make a habit of it. The previously mentioned firmness is essential. If a surveyor shows hesitancy or lack of confidence the first people to notice it, and possibly take advantage of it, will be the client and his advisers.

A surveyor must have a reasonable working knowledge of locks, bolts, bars, alarms, safes, etc., etc., or any specific form of security with which he is involved. Bearing in mind that many surveyors are composite, involving the various forms of security or even fire, liabilities and other subjects, to have a detailed knowledge of everything is asking a bit much. Remember, this book is for the comparative novice who is unlikely to be involved in the horrendous gold bullion type risk until he is much more experienced, and with experience comes greater detailed knowledge. In the early stages it is not necessary to know how many kilohertz this or that works at, but it is necessary to know when and, more importantly when not, to use the equipment involved.

How, then, does a surveyor arrive at his decision as to what degree and method of security is best suited to any particular premises or set of circumstances? The answer is not easy to put down on paper, but it is even more difficult to put into practice. He must amass a large number of facts, figures and other bits and pieces of information. He then inspects the premises in detail, not being afraid to ask to see behind locked doors. Having done all that, he should have a fairly good overall impression of the risk and it is only at that stage he can start evaluating and prescribing. If he tries to do it piecemeal as he goes around he will quite often find that one prescription is completely negated by something discovered later, and if he has already opened his mouth and pontificated he looks unnecessarily stupid having to retract his comments. Reading what has just been written, the job doesn't sound too difficult, does it? But think a bit deeper, all of the facts and figures assembled are going to, individually, have differing degrees of importance in each individual risk, *e.g.* a weakish rear door into an enclosed garden not easily accessible is not as dangerous as the same door on to a poorly lit access road running into a main road.

Every risk is unique, and for this reason I am totally against formally prescribed *"standards of security"*. You simply cannot have such standards until the day comes when you also have standard risks, standard burglars, and standard clients. Some insurers get round this by having *"guidelines"* for surveyors and underwriters, and even put them forward directly to clients, and, as long as they are used as such, they are all right. Unfortunately, in many cases, they are used as shields behind which surveyors, lacking in courage and imagination, hide. I have often seen protections which have come straight *"out of the book"* but, because of a peculiarity of the risk, are totally unsuitable and inappropriate.

Can you teach someone to be a surveyor? Not entirely. You can, and must, provide notes, lectures, demonstrations and the like. He will certainly need all of these, not only at the outset of his surveying career but as refreshers and updates throughout the rest of his surveying life. But that is only part of his armoury. He needs to have flair, imagination, diplomacy, the ability to see behind the obvious, and the other undefinable, unteachable abilities. Certainly, these can be encouraged and developed, but not taught, and without these you are left with a walking textbook with no character. One reason I feel these characteristics are essential is that the surveyor is, amongst other things, his employer's ambassador, representative, call him what you like. After all, he could be the only representative the client will ever see. In insurance, a surveyor has often been described as the underwriter's *"eyes and ears"*, but he is also his employer's *"mouth"*, an often forgotten fact. Diplomacy, or tact, is probably most necessary when dealing with private householders. Whilst extolling the virtues of good security, it is not necessary to leave the householder scared to death and frightened to answer the front door. You must also be prepared for the unusual. I remember, vividly, politely suggesting to a lady that the lock on her front door was not very good and could be improved without much cost. I was promptly condemned to eternal damnation: how dare I criticise her door lock, it had been recommended by her vicar who could do no wrong.

Right — now that you have amassed all of this information and come to your conclusions and decided what has to be done in the way of improvements (if anything — don't feel that you have to ask for something just to justify your existence, many risks will be acceptable as they are), what do you do now? You report all of the relevant, I repeat relevant, information to your employers in the form of a written report. The form in which this is done will obviously vary from employer to employer. What, you may ask is *"relevant information"*? Ah well, that depends upon the risk involved. The fact that a client has 3 children and a poodle is not relevant to a commercial risk, but very relevant to a domestic risk. The whole subject of reporting is dealt with in a later chapter.

Whether you are pushed for time, or just plain lazy, there is a very easy trap into which you might fall, ie that of excess brevity. It might not always be apparent to you because you have the advantage of having seen the premises and, therefore, know more than you are about to put in writing. What you might say, because of the *"information in your head"*, might seem reasonable to you, but the person reading the report does not have the information which is in your head. Purely as an example (there are many from which to choose), let us assume that you are asked to comment upon the type of area in which the risk is situated. Answers like *"commercial"* or *"residential"* or *"shopping"* are, in my opinion, completely useless. Is it good, poor, slum, top class etc, etc. Unless you tell the reader he is no better off than before your one word answer was given. I ask you quite simply to put yourself in the hallowed shoes of the reader and ask yourself what kind of picture are you painting, a clear one or a hazy one? Now that doesn't mean that you have to tell him about every brick and screw, there is a happy medium. Remember, you are inexperienced and it is only reasonable that the reader wants more information from you than he might require from a seasoned campaigner whom he knows and trusts — your time will come, if you stick to the job.

Unless your inside staff are 100% on the ball, and I refer to experience, not trustworthiness, there is certain information I would suggest that you do not commit to paper but should convey verbally. If you feel that the client is not trustworthy, but is crooked, or a *"fly man"*, or some other non-attractive person, any insurance underwriter should know this, but care must be taken that that opinion, and that is all that it is, an opinion (unless you have some definite information), cannot get back to the client or you might be on the wrong end of a lawsuit! I have, before now, refused to put certain information in writing, but have made sure that the correct person was informed.

If the surveyor is the eyes, ears and mouth, then the employer must be the rest of the body, and all parts of this body must work together for a heathly result. The other organs must provide back-up, information, opportunity to attend meetings, etc. Very few of these meetings are exactly a bundle of fun, yet some employers will not allow their surveyors to attend them unless they are out of business hours. I must say that the other side of the coin is also true, and some companies encourage attendance at such meetings, acknowledging that information gained will benefit the company as well as the individual; to me a much more enlightened attitude.

I have no doubt that some of what has been written above will not be acceptable to all. Good. I do not apologise. Hopefully, some thought and discussion may be stimulated.

CHAPTER 2
Risk Location Considerations

I feel that many surveyors are inclined to dive into a survey without reasonable preparation. I always try and arrive at a risk with at least 10 minutes to spare before an appointment. However, having done so, I do not sit reading the newspaper, nor do I go for a quick coffee. The object of *"spare time"* is to take an overall look at the premises, its neighbourhood, the local people and other general but essential considerations. You must remember that many losses arise not because of the fantastic value of the objects involved, but purely because they are in the wrong place at the wrong time. It can, therefore, pay handsome dividends to get an overall impression of the area by using your eyes to look around, and to look at any street map available.

The things you should be looking for include, age of building, with consequent probability of redevelopment, lack of prosperity with probability of unoccupancy, type of unoccupancies in the area, bearing in mind the type of people likely to be attracted thereto.

Let us go into these examples and other circumstances in greater detail.

If the area involved has very old buildings there is probably an increased likelihood of redevelopment. This can have several affects such as the buildings immediately adjoining that in which you are interested being demolished, which could mean the presence of scaffolding during such operations, thus making upper floors much more vulnerable than previously thought. It could also mean, even for a short time, that a wall becomes external and more vulnerable than was expected, especially if it was not built as, nor intended to be, an external wall. The older the building the more likelihood of re-roofing, face-lifts and the like, once again attracting scaffolding, a *"material fact"* which might justify the insurer refusing to meet a claim. Demolition in an adjoining street can result in an enclosed back yard no longer being enclosed. Be careful at this point not to confuse old age and redevelopment with *"run-down"*, the two need not be the same.

Having mentioned *"run-down"*, let us continue on this aspect. If the area is generally run-down and lacking in prosperity, there is more chance of the risks adjoining your client becoming vacant, thus increasing the possibility of an entry being made via a neighbouring property. In this type of area, once a building becomes vacant it often happens that it remains in that state for a long time, maybe even permanently. Run-down areas usually have houses which become empty for lengthy periods, or maybe even worse, attract the wrong type of resident who, at best, will not be helpful in reporting break-ins and, at worst, might be the type of person to actually commit the foul deed.

There can be a similar problem, ie empty shops, even in new and quite reasonable areas. I know of one where there are simply too many shop units for the local population, granted not helped by the recent development of a very large supermarket which has killed off some of the smaller shops. How do you foresee and cater for that?

Neighbourhood occupancies or activities can have profound affects on your risk, even if the problem source is half a mile distant. If, say, the shop you are surveying is on the direct route between a station and a soccer ground, there must be a chance that windows will be broken and, once broken, the display goods will disappear. Now standing outside the shop in question you may not see either the station or the stadium, hence the suggestion to look around and use maps. In such instances the goods involved need not be of extreme value or variety, all they need is to be present and visible. Having used a soccer ground as an example, remember there are other types of premises which could give rise to similar problems, *e.g.* discos, pubs, street markets, etc.

Street markets can present another problem. They often take place in quite narrow streets which are then congested with stalls, barrows and crowds looking around. It is, therefore, very easy for a hold-up man to disappear into these crowds and also very difficult, if not impossible, for police cars (and fire appliances) to get to the problem premises. Whilst many street markets operate virtually everyday, not all do, so you may be there on a non-market day and not be aware of tomorrow's problem. For regular markets, Monday is the favourite day off, especially if they have been open on the Sunday. These street markets and days involved are often signposted on traffic signs for motorists, so keep a look out for them.

Some local peculiarities have both good and bad points and the balance between the two is a matter for judgement at the time and place involved. An example is a one-way street system. This can mean that the burglar has restricted means of escape from the vicinity of his crime, but it also means that the police have restricted access to the same location. Assuming poor access to the rear of premises, it could be considered that an abnormally broad pavement to the front is a good thing as the burglar has further to carry his haul. True, but if he hears the law approaching he has more space to run away without having to venture onto the road with the risk of being run down. There are other considerations similar to those mentioned but they cannot all be listed.

One thing I like to see, although no doubt goods' deliverers disagree, is a raised pavement which has a very high kerb, or even steps. This must mean it is more difficult to use any vehicle as a battering ram to smash the shop front. Concrete bollards can also achieve this end but, before suggesting this, you must find out if local authorities will permit it to be done. If you suggest the impossible you don't do your reputation any good.

Most of the foregoing comments have been related to built-up areas such as towns, but we must not forget the rural or industrial estate type risk. I feel that in rural areas there is more of a community spirit and it is, therefore, more likely that the locals will treat the grocer, newsagent, etc. as *"their shop"*.

You will probably also find that small businesses employ local people, therefore any affect on that business could affect *"their job"*, the result being that the local population are more likely to react to suspicious persons or unusual happenings. This does not, however, mean that rural losses do not happen, but I think it is a plus factor. Unless you are talking about the big boys, it is probably reasonable to assume that the majority of burglars are town residents and less likely to know about the existence of specific country risks. However, if the burglar does get to know about the risk then it may be easier, just because of the openness of the area, to *"case the job"* and see the regular patterns of local life, an invaluable asset to crime planning. The obvious disadvantage of rural life is the warren of roads and tracks in which the burglar can lose himself and where the police are thinly spread and have further to travel to the scene of the crime, assuming of course the local P.C. is not too busy with foot and mouth disease control (surely that should be a Ministry of Agriculture responsibility — not the police).

Industrial estates have problems and advantages depending on the estate involved. Some are virtually open sites with buildings, *i.e.* unfenced, unsupervised and with no overall security. Even those sites with perimeter fences but no security personnel will almost inevitably end up with every tenant having keys to any gate, and each tenant having more than one such key. Depending on the number of tenants involved, the total number of keys can be quite considerable, with the net result of virtually no dependable security. On the other hand, you may be lucky enough to find your client within a tightly controlled, well secured complex. However, don't take too much for granted; just because there is a man in a uniform sitting in a gatehouse doesn't mean there is security. If you, without an appointment and without having to identify yourself, can get past the gateman without his referring to your client, then the security must be, at least, suspect. Even if the gateman does appear vigilant and diligent, you must enquire further: how many security personnel are on duty out of business hours?; what form of intercommunication do they have?; how often do they check with their base?; how often does the officer in charge have to check with an outside independent office?; what is the routine if any one of these checks is not made? If you are not happy with any of the answers you receive you may have to consider the estate as little better than one of the previously mentioned *"open site"* estates. Even if you are happy with the estate security, be careful not to place all your reliance on that. I am not, in these circumstances, running down any security organisations involved but, bearing in mind that you are hoping to protect your client for many years ahead, what happens if in the interim period the estate managers decide to dispense with that security organisation in favour of another less efficient firm or, even worse, dispense with any security at all? As your client may well have no say in the matter, would the change in security be a good enough reason for an insurer to avoid a claim?

A comparatively recent development is where former large factories have been converted into many, sometimes very many, smaller units. Often, partitioning walls are quite thin and certainly not as thick as normal external walls. Many of these units are taken on by businesses which are just starting up, and as many either (i) fail, or (ii) prosper and transfer to larger premises,

9

the turnover of tenants (and therefore hazard and underoccupancy) can be quite great. Also, as most of the unit doors are internal to the main structure, seclusion is automatic for someone who has gained entry to the main building and is then trying to get into a particular unit. How many keys are there to the main doors?

Regardless of whether you are involved with a town risk, a rural risk or an industrial estate risk, proximity to motorways and other major roads has in the past been considered a relevant feature. I am not convinced of the relevance of this argument; any road is good enough to make a getaway and, with major roadways spreading, few risks are all that remote from good transport facilities. How often have you heard on television, especially in connection with armed hold-up, that the getaway car has been found abandoned within half a mile of the incident, no motorways or anything similar being involved?

Having so far concerned ourselves with overall local considerations, let us now concentrate on the external factors more close to the actual risk itself. Try your best to look around the risk from the outside, see how much is visible from other people's premises — whatever you can see so can a potential burglar. If you can gain access to rear garden or yard from a lane, private or public, then so can a burglar, but, equally importantly, so can the police. One problem which does arise fairly frequently is a break-in to the rear of the premises, but the police cannot gain entry to the rear without climbing walls or going through private property. Some police forces give specific instructions to their policemen not to do so, so that even if an alarm is raised the police can do little but stand outside the front awaiting the keyholder whilst the burglars, with less scruples about other people's property, are making their getaway. The only way the police could combat this eventuality would be to flood the area with policemen and, as you know, this is just not practicable.

From strolling around outside, you can often see blocked-up doors and windows which are not visible from the inside due to decoration, panelling or stock arranged on shelving around walls. You may see trap-doors or pavement lights into a basement the client does not use, or which may not be accessible from his premises. From the outside you may also see external fire escapes, balconies etc., from other buildings, which give access to your client. There are many things you may see which put you on your guard when inside the building, and may give rise to questions to ask the client you would otherwise have missed.

The reverse of this process may also be necessary in that, having once been inside the buildings, you may be sufficiently put on your guard that you have to have a second look from the outside to clarify matters.

The risk you are surveying may turn out to be fairly innocuous in itself, but may be immediately next door to a much heavier risk, *e.g.* a jeweller, tobacconist or the like, consequently your risk may be broken into as a route into the heavy risk. I accept there is a probably very little you can do to prevent this (it is not really practicable to alarm a florist's shop because of the occupancy of its neighbour), but it is relevant information which should be passed on as insurance considerations may arise.

This is one of the aspects where I feel Insurers do not help themselves. They appear to be horrified at the idea of compelling their Insured to tell them of changes to his immediate neighbours. I know of a case where the upper floors were empty and being extensively renovated during winter (although they had been fully occupied when surveyed) — guess what?, the withdrawal of the heating for a prolonged period caused a burst pipe in the unoccupied portion, causing water damage to the rest of the building and its contents. There must be many similar losses from burglary due to unoccupancy etc. Why do Insurers not insist upon being told of these vital factors? Could it be due to such elements as competition, Broker power etc, or am I just being cynical?

So far in this chapter we have been *"sizing up"* the risk from a physical aspect. You also have to size up some aspects of the client and his organisation — it could be termed *"accessability"*.

It sometimes horrifies me the number of occasions where I have been able to talk myself into a risk without seeing someone in authority, without having to prove my identity and without an appointment. If that on its own were sufficient grounds for declining an insurance risk, I could reduce my employer's portfolio by 25/30% with no trouble. I am not a silver tongued conversationalist, so if I can do it so can others, including potential burglars. I must confess that many years ago I spent nearly an hour surveying a risk and came out with full details of the contents, alarm and other protections, together with full details of cash handling methods and the like. There was only one snag — I shouldn't have been on the premises in the first place. I had gone to the wrong address, same surname of Insured and same trade (it was a predominantly *"rag trade area"*)!

Don't be fooled by business cards, and your clients shouldn't be either. You can have them printed in any small printers without any questions at all. It seems to be generally accepted that appointments should be made to carry out surveys and that is what I inferred a short while ago. There is a lot to be said for appointments to prevent waste of time etc, but are you seeing the true risk, or are you seeing a version which has been "tarted up" for your presence. I have visited premises where there was not a single thing out of place and not one piece of waste on the floor, which showed brushmarks. Somehow, it was not very realistic.

Throughout all this observation procedure you must use your imagination (but don't let it run away with you). Discos, pubs and other mass audience/participant places are often not open when you are in the area — look for them, they won't look for you.

CHAPTER 3

Doors — Construction

It is arguable which is the most vulnerable point of entry of any building, so no relevance should be placed on the order in which they are tackled. I will start with doors, purely because they are usually the largest (physically) legal means of entry. At this stage the door construction will be considered but no mention made of door fixings or locking devices as they will be covered in later chapters, where they can be related to all doors described.

Doors

The variety of types of door is quite considerable and, unfortunately, although each door has a specific role to play it is not uncommon to find them in completely different situations from that intended by the manufacturer or designer. Consequently, they may be asked to perform a role for which they were never intended, a good example being internal doors used as external doors in offices and shops. One can only assume the *'cowboys'* have done a good sales job, or that the doors *'were going cheap'*, security and suitability not even being considered.

Certain doors are not too easy to identify properly because of decoration, linings, facings etc., so don't be too quick to jump to rash conclusions when you first see any particular door.

I will now consider the most commonly encountered types of door, but you can rest assured that you will find others not covered in this book, hopefully not too often.

All Timber Doors
A   Rebate panelled — see figure 1. The stiles, rails and muntins can vary from 1″ to 2″ or 3″ in thickness, depending upon whether the door is intended for internal or external use. The panels are always much thinner than the stiles (they can be as thin as ⅛″) and are usually of thin wood, plywood or hardboard. The panels are usually held in place by one of two methods, viz (1) by slotting into grooves in the stile at the time of manufacture — consequently more costly to repair (at least to the same appearance) if the door has to be reassembled for just one damaged panel. Method (2) is by pinned beading which is much easier to repair and replace, but also much easier and quieter to remove for illegal purposes.

You may encounter panels which are reasonably thick in the middle and bevelled down to the edges and fixings, but these are no stronger from a security aspect (as opposed to accidental damage) as the fixing position is the critical point.

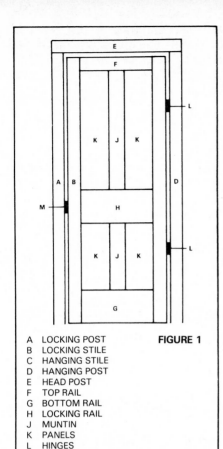

A LOCKING POST   **FIGURE 1**
B LOCKING STILE
C HANGING STILE
D HANGING POST
E HEAD POST
F TOP RAIL
G BOTTOM RAIL
H LOCKING RAIL
J MUNTIN
K PANELS
L HINGES
M LOCK BOLT

NOTES
(1) SOMETIMES 'K' HAS ORNAMENTAL
    BEADING
(2) SOMETIMES A D AND E ARE COVERED
    WITH ORNAMENTAL BEADING CALLED
    ARCHITRAVE
(3) THE *'STILES'* AND *'RAILS'* VARY IN
    THICKNESS FROM 1″ to 3″.

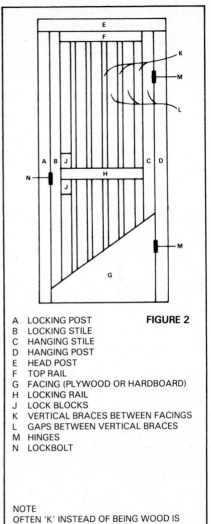

A LOCKING POST   **FIGURE 2**
B LOCKING STILE
C HANGING STILE
D HANGING POST
E HEAD POST
F TOP RAIL
G FACING (PLYWOOD OR HARDBOARD)
H LOCKING RAIL
J LOCK BLOCKS
K VERTICAL BRACES BETWEEN FACINGS
L GAPS BETWEEN VERTICAL BRACES
M HINGES
N LOCKBOLT

NOTE
OFTEN 'K' INSTEAD OF BEING WOOD IS
LITERALLY EGG BOXES (IN ADDITION TO 'L')

B   Flush panelled. This is largely the same as door A above, but there is one very important difference *viz*, the panels on one side of the door are flush with the stiles, the joints being covered with beading. However, if the reverse side of this door is viewed it will have the appearance of door A, so the surveyor must view every door from both sides, or if for some reason this is not possible then it may well be prudent to err on the side of caution.

C   Flush – see figure 2. The stiles, rails and muntins are similar to those in A above. The braces are, in most cases, fairly weak and far apart and the intervening gaps may be empty or filled with egg boxes or similar weak material. The stiles, rails, muntins, braces and infill materials are all covered with either hardboard or plywood, so the viewer has literally no idea of the thickness or quality of any of the component parts. Personally, I work on the basis that *'unless someone can prove me to be wrong I must assume the worst features to be present'*.

D Solid — In this type of door the panels are the same thickness as the stiles etc., but not necessarily of the same type of wood. The description is often thought to mean that the door is one single piece of timber, which it can be but seldom is. There is another danger which is that the panels may have the appearance of being the same thickness as the stiles but may be only two relatively thin pieces of wood flush with the stiles, having an air space between them. This difference can *sometimes* be detected by gently swinging the door on its hinges and trying to stop the door swing with one finger. You must then try and judge by the force the door exerts on your finger whether the door is heavy enough to be solid. This is *not* an easy or foolproof method of detection, but it is more likely to be acceptable to a client then drilling holes in his door!

E Ledged and Braced — see figure 3. These are vertical strips of comparatively thin timber, held together by slightly thicker timbers to which they are nailed or screwed, the thicker timbers being the horizontals and diagonals on the inside of the door. In the majority of instances these doors will be external and subject to weathering. If you ally this factor to comparatively thin, low standard, timber used, deterioration is often fairly rapid and one of the first signs is the loosening of nails and screws, so an originally weak door becomes even weaker. The only way to overcome this is exceptionally good maintenance, and if the door is fairly new when first inspected by the surveyor, he has no way of knowing whether such maintenance will be done. A resurvey several years later may be too late.

   In some cases you will find the doors with no diagonal braces making an even weaker product.

F Ledged, Framed and Braced — see figure 4. Very similar to E above, except that there is a frame all round the door, and no top and bottom rail.

   The door is stronger than E above and the frame makes lock fitting easier. The illustrations and above comments regarding E and F are mainly aimed at "normal sized" doors, but you will encounter very large versions at loading bays and the like. From a structural aspect the only difference is that the materials used will, or should, be stronger and thicker.

Timber and Glass Doors

Let us first of all consider the types of glass most likely to be encountered in timber framed doors, although obviously other types of glass may be found on more rare occasions.

Sheet glass is probably the most commonly found, but one of the most difficult problems (also with windows) is assessing the thickness of the glass involved as the edge of the glass cannot be seen. I have heard of many *'methods'* of thickness detection, *e.g.* holding a 10p piece at right angles to the glass and estimating the thickness of the reflection of the edge of the 10p

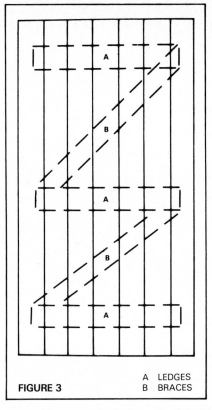

FIGURE 3

A   LEDGES
B   BRACES

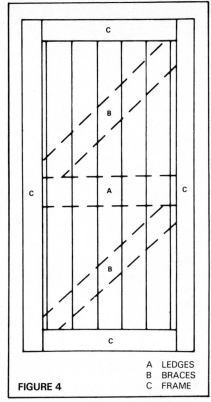

FIGURE 4

A   LEDGES
B   BRACES
C   FRAME

piece. However, I admit to treating this type of method with suspicion. There are cardboard and plastic cards available which are marked so that reflections in the glass can be read along graduated lines to indicate the thickness. Being thin and brittle, sheet glass is very easy to break, or even to cut, with very little noise.

Other forms of glass are easier to recognise, the most obvious being wired glass. However, wired glass is often used as a general term and can therefore be misinterpreted by the reader of a report if more detail is not given. *'Wired glass'* is fairly weak as the wire used is virtually *'chicken wire'* which is very easy to break or cut if exposed. *'Georgian Wired Glass'* contains steel wire, welded at its intersections and slightly stronger than ordinary wired glass. Electro-copper glass is very similar to Georgian Wired Glass, except that the wire used is placed in a copper plating tank for at least 24 hours. In all cases the wire is embedded in the glass at the time of manufacture and not *'added on'* later. From a security aspect the glass cannot be considered strong, but, from a fire aspect the wire tends to hold the fractured glass together.

Leaded glass is plain or coloured sheet or plate glass of varying shapes and sizes held together in lead H section channelling, known as *'cames'*, within the door (or window) frame. The cames are very easy to cut or prise open

15

with a sharp knife or similar implement, so the glass can be removed in almost complete silence. A note of caution however, there is a current fashion to make ordinary glass panels look like leaded glass by the surface application of lead or plastic strips. If expertly done it is not easy to tell the difference, but gentle pressure on the centre of the glass with the fingers shows that genuine leaded glass will *'give'* considerably, the imitation hardly at all. I strongly advise the use of a handkerchief between the finger and the glass, unless you want to leave an irate customer complaining about your finger marks on his glass.

Apart from the most obvious, *i.e.* a single sheet of glass in a timber frame, glass panelled doors are found in different forms the more common of which are illustrated in figure 5. Where there is part glass and part timber panelling, virtually without exception the glass will be nearer the top of the door, the

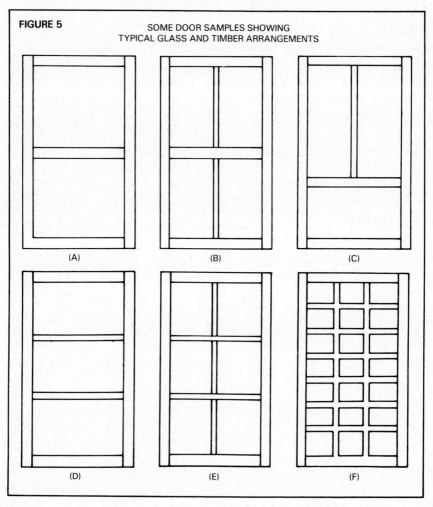

FIGURE 5 SOME DOOR SAMPLES SHOWING TYPICAL GLASS AND TIMBER ARRANGEMENTS

(A)   (B)   (C)

(D)   (E)   (F)

sizes and proportions varying enormously. Although it is not an invariable rule, you will more often than not discover that the greater the number of panels (glass or timber) in a door, the thinner are the timber spars separating these panels. This can be very important, especially with a door similar to that shown in figure 5(f), because a break at the junction of four neighbouring panes of glass loosens all four panes and, although individually each pane may be small, four together can produce an opening through which an intruder could pass fairly easily. These spars can be broken accidentally, say by children playing or by the door slamming in a wind, and if not a complete break repairs may be *'put off'*, thus producing an invitation to the burglar to complete the job.

A type of door being encountered more frequently nowadays, especially in places where Fire Authorities have become involved, is the Fire Check Door. These provide a certain resistance to fire spread, varying with the occupation involved. The actual construction of the doors varies, often containing elements of some fire resistant material and wired glass. Unfortunately, because of their fire properties the occupant of the premises quite often gains a false impression of the physical strength of the door. It is essential with this type of door to get fire authority approval *before* any security devices are affixed thereto. It shows surveyors in a poor light if they prescribe devices which could result in the client getting into trouble, possibly even leading to loss of life.

Metal Doors (excluding aluminium framed doors)

A   Some doors constructed of all metal are made from sheet metal on an angle iron frame, very similar in design to the ledged, braced and framed timber door. However, the metal is usually in one sheet (per leaf), or more seldom, in two sheets being joined along the centre ledge (see figure 4). In the construction of these doors (assuming reasonable strength materials have been used), probably the most important factor is how the sheet metal and angle iron frame are joined to each other. The most satisfactory method is for the sheet to be welded to *all* sections of the angle iron frame (*i.e.* to the braces and the frame. It is not uncommon to find the fixing having been done to the frame only) and not just the outer sections, the welding points not being further than 12" apart. If welding is, for some reason, not used then the next best method is the use of coach bolts, the spacing being as for welding, with all nuts being internal. Unfortunately, ordinary nuts and bolts are often used and, if so, *all* of the bolt heads must be spot welded to prevent removal, but this method is not as good as using coach bolts in the first place. The foregoing sounds fairly simple and straightforward, doesn't it? But, unless a professional does the job, wrong results can arise. I clearly recollect a case where I asked for coach bolts and they were used. However, the type used had a square shoulder beneath the dome head, but no hole had been made to accommodate the shoulder so all the heads stood out awaiting the burglar's hacksaw!

A third method encountered is the use of non return or "clutch" screws and, if used, they should not be further apart than 9". The sheet metal *must* have the screw holes countersunk otherwise the screwheads will stand proud, once again an invitation to the hacksaw.

A common fault with this type of door, even when the correct materials and methods of construction are used, is that the door itself is too large, resulting in twisting and distortion which, over a period of time, must result in the door being weakened.

You will also encounter cases where corrugated iron has been used instead of sheet metal. Corrugated iron has neither the strength nor ease of fixing of sheet metal and its use should always be discouraged.

B   Metal roller shutters are also a commonly encountered *'all metal door'* (see figure 6). Basically they consist of many strips of metal, jointed together in such a way as to allow them to form themselves into a roll, like broadloom carpet. The metal strips slot or slide into metal runners down either side of the opening to keep them in an orderly position, which also provides some of the strength. The last strip of metal, *i.e.* that closest to the ground when the shutter is closed, is usually attached to a piece of angle iron which then lies flush on the ground or floor. To achieve this where the ground slope is quite severe may necessitate really expert design, as opposed to the more general, virtually mass produced variety. When *'open'* the roll of strips is housed in a metal box if mounted externally, no housing if mounted internally. The runners in which the shutter is guided, and the box housing, if present, are just as important a feature of security as the shutter itself. This is a point frequently overlooked by less scrupulous installers. There must be sufficient fixings to prevent removal from the brickwork or other material to which they are attached; there must be no gap between the runner and the brickwork otherwise a hacksaw can be used on these fixings. The heads of any fixing screws must be either *'non-return'* in design (and countersunk) or completely hidden when the shutter is closed. These latter points may seem obvious, but just look at your local high street and see how often they are ignored.

Where these shutters are the final exit from a building you will find a small single leaf door therein, i.e. the *'wicket gate'*. This is of the same material as the rest of the shutter, but is on its own frame which can be released internally and swung away from the shutter to allow it to be rolled up.

Sometimes shutters have an *'open brickwork'* pattern (see figure 7), where, instead of metal strips, you have rods and tie bars forming a larger shutter full of *'holes'*. These are more usually found protecting windows, or at the front window line where there is a lobby behind, with recessed doors. Sometimes, but not often, you may find them in enclosed shopping centres, with no lobby or door behind them, and to me this is undesirable as if someone does gain access to the centre they can put lighted materials through the holes. A point of very serious caution − where these shutters are installed externally Local Planning Permission is necessary, and if not obtained your client may be forced to have them removed. It is essential that your client be informed of this if you prescribe them; if you do not, you could in effect be instructing your client to break the law − not very clever.

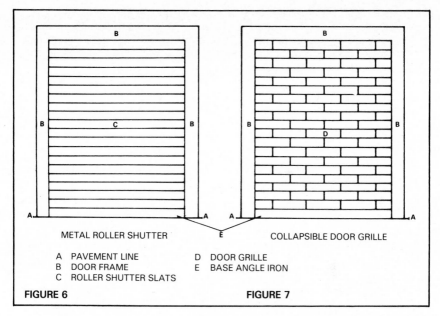

METAL ROLLER SHUTTER   E   COLLAPSIBLE DOOR GRILLE

A PAVEMENT LINE   D DOOR GRILLE
B DOOR FRAME   E BASE ANGLE IRON
C ROLLER SHUTTER SLATS

FIGURE 6   **FIGURE 7**

C A door working on similar principles to the metal roller shutter is the *'folding metal door'*. Solid metal sections are hinged vertically and instead of *'rolling up'* they fold, concertina style, to the side of the door opening. They are held in place not by runners at the side of the door, but top and bottom.

D Another form of all metal door, met within buildings as opposed to being on the perimeter, is the Fireproof Door made to FOC or Local Authority specification. As these specifications are very exact it is unwise to meddle with them by affixing locks etc., as to do so may impair their fireproof qualities (*e.g.* by the boring of holes for screws etc.). The only time I would think it reasonable to do so is if the door is present but no longer used for its fireproof qualities. Such doors should have plates on them stating to what specification they have been made, but in all cases they are usually very strong.

Note – all metal doors are *'made to measure'* and therefore not easy to amend on site if inaccurately made. It follows that replacement costs are higher than with timber doors which can be planed etc. if fractionally too large.

E Glass panelled metal framed doors of various types are quite common. Although the metal is usually much thinner than the timber used in similar doors, the metal itself is much stronger assuming it is properly maintained. It is not uncommon, however, if the door is directly facing the sun, for the metal to expand and contract and this can cause the glass to crack in what appears mysterious circumstances. The frames, if not properly maintained, will rust and distort and this is a greater problem to repair than lack of maintenance in timber doors. The glass panels usually fit into grooves within the metal or are held in place by glazing putty which is easy to remove with a sharp implement. Regrettably, this putty is quite often found on the outer surfaces of the door making it (a) more liable to weathering defects, and (b) accessible for picking and removal. Internal putty is much preferable from a security aspect, but admittedly not so pleasing to the eye. Any type of glass you will find in timber framed doors is likely to be found in metal framed doors.

F Metal Railed (not framed) doors — see figure 8. As you will see the rail is at the top and bottom only, the sides being exposed. The glass is invariably ¼" thick *'armoured plate'*. This term on its own can cause trouble as the client usually has false impressions of its strength. It is strong but by no means impregnable, and a pointed implement can cause complete collapse into granules without too much force being applied (very similar to many car windscreens). The one advantage to this type of door is that the surveyor can actually see the edge of the glass and measure it. If the pane of glass is sufficiently large it will actually bend to a certain degree. Because there are no locking stiles you will almost certainly have a gap between the door and its frame, and with no rebates etc., on a stormy night you could have draughts which could interfere with Intruder Alarm protection.

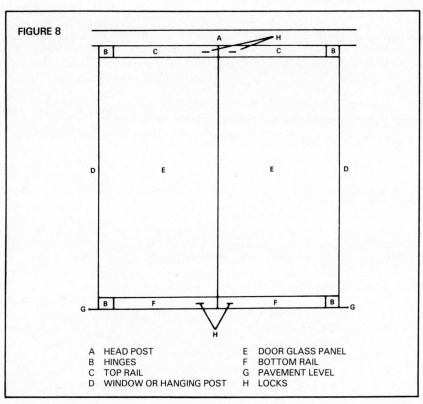

FIGURE 8

A HEAD POST
B HINGES
C TOP RAIL
D WINDOW OR HANGING POST
E DOOR GLASS PANEL
F BOTTOM RAIL
G PAVEMENT LEVEL
H LOCKS

Aluminium Framed Doors
Aluminium Framed Doors are a comparatively recent but very fast spreading form of door, especially in shop fronts, offices and private dwellings. Unlike the other metal doors, the metal frame is of hollow rectangular section. The metal used, *i.e.* aluminium, is comparatively soft and therefore easy to damage accidentally or intentionally, with consequent replacement costs. The glass in these doors is usually laminated, *i.e.* two sheets of glass with a layer of plastic between, and the doors are very often double glazed.

General Notes
Much mention has just been made of door construction, but it follows that regardless of how the door is built, it loses much, if not all, of its strength and usefulness if it is not well maintained. A rotting door of any kind must never be accepted.

Just as important, but seldom mentioned, is the condition of the door frame to which the door is attached. You cannot take it for granted that a good door will have an equally good frame. The door might have been replaced at some time, but nothing may have been done to the frame for years. Even a door frame in apparently good condition will be useless if it is not well affixed to the adjoining building. It can be virtually impossible to tell just how well a frame has been installed and all that I can suggest is that you look for obvious defects like daylight between the frame and the building, or if you can move the frame even a little by just using your fingers (a burglar will use something stronger), then the frame requires immediate attention, by a specialist, not the local handyman.

CHAPTER 4

Door Fittings

The previous chapter mentioned the actual doors, and a later chapter will deal with the securing of the doors. This chapter deals with two aspects which fall into neither of these categories, viz door fittings and securing devices which are not locks. In the case of door fittings, I feel that they are seldom mentioned in reports and think that that is probably on the assumption that if not mentioned they will be O.K. – I wonder if it is because they have never been examined?

Hinges etc.

All doors must be attached to door frames by some method and, for convenience of operation, the most obvious is by hinges. However, there are different types of hinge, and unless the correct one is used in any particular situation the most likely result would be a door of doubtful security value.

The Butt hinge (see figure 9) is the most commonly used on timber framed doors, and can also be used on metal doors if there is sufficient breadth of frame for attachment. These hinges come in many sizes ranging from very small (only suitable for furniture doors) to quite large. Because most jobs are done with cost saving in mind it is quite often the case that hinges which are too small are used, the criterion for hinge size being the weight of the door. It is fairly obvious that if the hinge is too weak it will break sooner or later, and even before that occurs it could be a weak spot capitalised upon by a burglar. It is also obvious that if a hinge has 8 screw holes then 8 screws should be used. I recently encountered a shop door where each hinge had 2 screws and 6 empty holes, but no-one in the shop had even noticed.

The pin holding the two halves of the hinge together is known as the hinge pin. In most cases it is not too difficult to knock this pin out, thus reducing the hinge to two useless pieces of metal. With outward opening doors the hinge pin is exposed to the outside and, therefore, to the potential burglar. This can be countered by the use of hinge bolts, mentioned later in this chapter.

Where these hinges are used on metal framed doors the best way of attachment to the door (and door

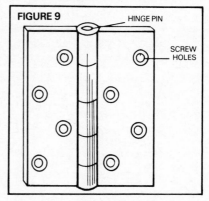

FIGURE 9   HINGE PIN

SCREW HOLES

frame if it too is metal) is by welding. Bear in mind that metal doors are usually heavier than timber doors of similar size, so larger hinges or more hinges will be necessary. Hinge bolts can be welded to metal doors.

The T or Tee Hinge (see figure 10) is most commonly associated with garden gates. This type of hinge is also frequently used on ledged and braced doors (not necessarily on ledged, braced and framed doors where butt hinges can be used). Usually they are made from thin metal which, if not properly fixed to the door, can be prized therefrom and torn or cut. It is essential, therefore, that all screw holes are used. The hinge is always fitted on the side of the door in which direction the door opens, so if you are dealing with outward opening doors the hinge will be outside — non-return screws must be used in **all** screwholes. It is not sufficient to use them only in some of the holes with ordinary screws in the remainder, as is sometimes done.

There are some rare occasions where the ledges go the full breadth of the door in which case butt hinges and hinge bolts can be used, but this does not happen very often.

Hook and Hinge (see figure 11) could be considered as the big brother of the T hinge, but the differences are very important. The most important factor is the strength of the metal. In this case it is quite thick and strong, although possibly more brittle. This strength enables it to be used on much larger doors, *e.g.* the large ledged and braced doors found in garages and warehouses where T hinges would be totally inadequate and where butt hinges might also be too weak. As the name and illustration suggests the part of the hinge which fits onto the door frame has the appearance of a hook, this being formed by the hinge pin which is an integral part of the plate which is attached to the frame. The part of the hinge which fits onto the door literally rests upon this *'hook'*, its own weight keeping it down. From this description you will realise that if there is sufficient strength available the door can be lifted off its hinge, so once again hinge bolts are desirable if they can be fitted. Like the T hinge, these hinges are fitted on the side of the door in the direction in which it is opened so they are external on outward opening doors. As you would by now expect, this requires coach bolts and non return screws to be used. If there is a coach bolt hole, then it must be used for a coach bolt, and

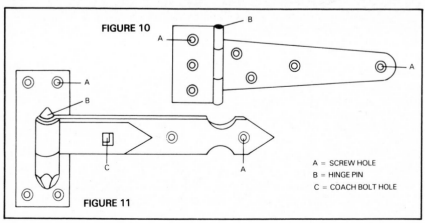

FIGURE 10

FIGURE 11

A = SCREW HOLE
B = HINGE PIN
C = COACH BOLT HOLE

not a screw as I have seen.

There is a variation on this hinge where it is made in one piece, there being a top to the hinge pin, preventing the door being *'lifted off its hinges'*. In such cases hinge bolts are not so necessary.

As a point of general interest you may encounter, as I have, instances where T hinges or hook and hinge hinges have been welded onto the metal sheet of an all metal door. In my opinion this is wrong. I think it is a fair assumption that in most cases the coach bolts etc. which are holding the sheet metal onto the angle iron frame will have been chosen to do that job and no other. If the hinge is welded onto the sheet metal then the frame is not *'attached'* to the door frame in any way and the weight (in some cases quite considerable) is being borne by the aforementioned coach bolts etc., and as they were not chosen for this purpose you will probably end up with distortion, fracturing etc.

Sliding doors do not have hinges, but they do have runners. The weight of the door is taken by a runner at the top of the door, an example of which is in Figure 12, although there are variations. There are obviously several of these depending upon the size and weight of the door. Where the door is double leaf there should be a fixed block or stopper in the centre of the rail to prevent one leaf *'straying'* onto the area intended for the other leaf.

Do not overlook this point. The slamming action of closing this type of door against the stopper can, after a while, result in the stopper being broken off. Unfortunately, in many cases the doors concerned can be very tall and it can be difficult to actually see the stopper. If in doubt you are quite within your rights to ask for the door to be closed to see that one is present and working.

You will find many doors of this type where there isn't, and never has been, a stopper. The *'straying'* action can be prevented by one, or both, of the leaves being internally secured to the door frame when closed. This is satisfactory if the securing device is adequate (but more often than not it is inadequate) eg. a padlocking bolt (mentioned later) and on the condition that it is always used.

In similar doors, which are in effect folding doors, then the same principle applies but the runners are allocated per section of the door. As well as the top runner there is a guide rail embedded in the ground or floor. A rigid metal probe should project from the foot of the door into this rail which acts as a *'guide'*. Without this guide the door would just hang loose from the top runner, could be pushed or pulled away from its vertical plane and someone could crawl underneath. A common fault is the bottom rail becoming filled with dirt and rubbish impairing proper use, and the probes at the foot of the door being broken off or bent.

Hinge Bolts (sometimes known as dog bolts) — see figure 13 — have been mentioned several times in preceding paragraphs. They are devices where a rigid metal projection is screwed onto the hinge edge of the door and a bolt hole is made in the hinge post, so that when the door is closed the two fit perfectly. There are two main reasons for using these devices: (a) where the hinge pin is exposed and liable to be removed this provides a *'securing device'* as it means the door cannot be opened from the hinge side; and (b) just to provide additional strength to a door which might be thought to be especially

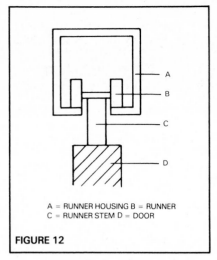

A = RUNNER HOUSING B = RUNNER
C = RUNNER STEM D = DOOR

FIGURE 12

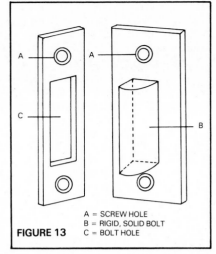

FIGURE 13

A = SCREW HOLE
B = RIGID, SOLID BOLT
C = BOLT HOLE

liable to attack. It is often used, wrongly in my opinion, for a third reason, *viz,* as a supplement where the hinges present are thought to be inadequate for the task involved. I think this is wrong for two reasons: (i) it is contrary to the rule that the hinges must be fit for the job or they should be replaced; (ii) it only gives support when the door is closed; when open it is useless, so distortion etc. will still take place if the hinges are inadequate.

These hinge bolts can be obtained in several sizes, so once again the correct one for the task involved must be chosen. To do otherwise is false security and false economy.

Note − One point over which the surveyor has virtually no control, but which is very important, is the length of screws used with door fixings. The fact that a screw head completely fills a screwhole in a piece of equipment does not guarantee that the screw is of adequate length to provide sufficient *'grip'*. Short of removing the screws (all of them) to inspect them, a move I **do not** recommend, I know of no method of overcoming this problem. It would appear to be something we have to *'live with'*. This problem does, of course, also apply to locks etc.

Doorway protection

One problem, which in certain circumstances can be major, is the passage of vehicles, heavy trolleys and the like through doorways. It is quite easy to imagine this problem with large doors which virtually invite such traffic, but don't be caught on the hop, the same problem can happen with single leaf, normal sized doors when you consider trolleys.

Of course the problem to which I refer is damage caused by operators whose accuracy leaves a lot to be desired. Some only appear to be aware that their implement is too large after having tried and failed to make the required entrance. The unfortunate result is that the door and/or frame is struck by the trolley, and if it happens often enough, or with sufficient force, a once good and suitable door or frame can be greatly reduced in efficiency and become an open invitation to the would-be intruder to *'have a go'*. This is probably as good a juncture as any to consider ways of reducing this potential problem. With the larger doors you must consider the top of the door as well as the edges or sides.

For the sides you should consider metal or concrete bollards immediately in line with the outermost part of the door or frame when the door is open. The idea is, of course, that the bollard would be struck before the door or frame. If thinking of large lorries or trucks you must remember that the doorway could be broad enough, but not tall enough. You therefore have to consider suspending metal bollards or the like from the top of the doorway. This is especially important if the door in question is sliding, and the likely point of impact is the door runners. With this it is advisable to have the bollard slightly lower than the frame, and not in line as with those at the sides. The reason is that a laden lorry entering and unloading will ride slightly higher when leaving.

Hopefully, the impact with one of these bollards will be enough to stop the driver from going further. Remember, in some large establishments vehicles go in one door and out another. In this case you might have to consider internal bollards on the door where the exit is made. If the vehicle goes in and out the same door then they might have to be on both sides of the one door.

In the case of normal single leaf doors, the problem is more likely to be runaway trolleys. I use the word runaway not in a derogatory manner, but ask you to think of some of the trolleys you must use at supermarkets; they appear to have a mind of their own, and the heavier the load, the more determined that stubborn mind becomes. In these cases it is likely that the problem is going to be at the door sides, and less likely, but not impossible, at the top. Initially you might think that the same measures as described above will be required, but I think not. The power used is likely to be less, and the measures to be taken can be more modest. In most circumstances the problem can be solved by angle iron on the door frame (but make sure that it does not interfere with the door closing properly). The most notable exceptions to this idea are where the door is either a metal roller shutter (or protected by same) or a door which does not open through a full 180 deg. (and is not obstructed from doing so). In the first case the runners would be vulnerable and in the second it would be the hinge edge of the door which is in danger. In these circumstances you may well have to resort to the bollards, but probably of a lesser strength specification.

Fork lift trucks fall somewhere between the two situations quoted above, and you may have to work that one out on site.

Securing devices – not locks

Some securing devices which you will encounter will now be described but, in my opinion, they should not be considered locks, merely additional aids to security.

(i)   Amongst the most common are *'bolts'*, i.e. Barrel and Tower bolts as illustrated in figures 14 and 15 respectively. These are basically the same, only the design detail being different. A rod of metal glides through a tube on the door frame, the rod thus forming a bar across the door and door frame.

Several defects occur with these devices. Often the staple is not fitted to the door frame, but a hole is bored therein leaving very little wood around the hole to provide resistance to physical force. The door *'sags'* and the bolt only goes into the staple a mere fraction of an inch, and as long as this happens nothing is done to rectify the situation. You will encounter some cheaper versions without bolt stops, allowing the bolt to come out of the guides completely and become lost.

A better version, assuming it is properly fitted and used, is that illustrated in figure 16 *i.e.* a padlocking bolt. It is basically the same as a barrel bolt except that a padlock can be fitted to prevent its being opened except by someone with the correct key.

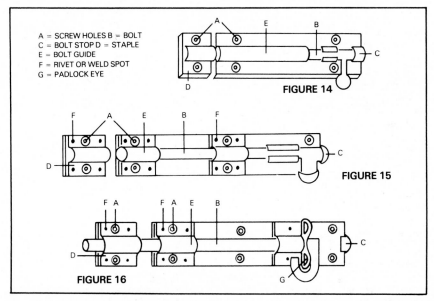

A = SCREW HOLES B = BOLT
C = BOLT STOP D = STAPLE
E = BOLT GUIDE
F = RIVET OR WELD SPOT
G = PADLOCK EYE

FIGURE 14

FIGURE 15

FIGURE 16

(ii) A Flush bolt works on the same principle as the previously described bolts but the essential difference is that it is set into the door and lies flush with the door surface as illustrated in figure 17. It is at its most effective in double leaf doors where the bolt is in the edge of the first closing leaf, thus when the door is closed it is hidden and unable to be manipulated.

Regrettably you will often find these fitted on the inner surface of the door, and not on the edge. To my mind, where there is any glass

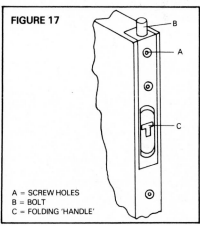

FIGURE 17

A = SCREW HOLES
B = BOLT
C = FOLDING 'HANDLE'

27

in close proximity such fitting negates one of the main advantages, *i.e.* the bolt becomes readily accessible again and easy to operate illegally. I can only assume when this is done it is either in complete ignorance, or sheer laziness as edge fitting is a bit more difficult.

(iii) Panic bolts (or panic bars), as illustrated in figure 18, are usually found on doors forming part of a Fire Exit Route. To a large extent they work on the same principle as barrel or tower bolts, *i.e.* a bolt fitting into the head post and another into the floor. However, these two bolts are connected to each other and operate at the same instant and move the same distance as each other. To operate these bolts pressure is applied to a horizontally mounted bar with the bolts being attached thereto in a hinged manner. The pressure removes the bolts from the staple or hole. Some of the bolts fit into holes in the upper door frame (where it would not be possible to fit staples). However, as usual, the hole must be properly positioned with sufficient wood left to provide some strength. Some of these bolts have a rimlatch incorporated therein but collectively they cannot be considered to provide good security. However, the surveyor must be extremely careful before requiring additional locks or devices to be fitted, as to do so may be a direct contravention of Fire Regulations. **I cannot over-emphasise the need for extreme care when dealing with Fire Exit Doors.**

(iv) An Espagnolette bolt (see figure 19) is a variation of the panic bar but not with the same intention, *i.e.* Fire Exit control. Once again we have a bar moving up and down into staples or holes in the floor, but this is operated by a simple handle. This is an old fashioned type of securing device but is still found in older types of buildings, usually private houses.

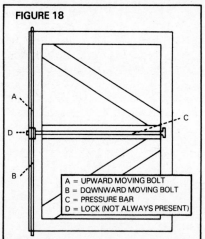

FIGURE 18

A = UPWARD MOVING BOLT
B = DQWNWARD MOVING BOLT
C = PRESSURE BAR
D = LOCK (NOT ALWAYS PRESENT)

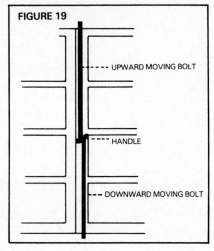

FIGURE 19

- - - - UPWARD MOVING BOLT

- - - - HANDLE

- - DOWNWARD MOVING BOLT

General Note

A point to be borne in mind wherever you have a bolt moving down into the ground or floor is that the hole will invariably become full of dirt so that the bolt cannot operate properly. It will then either fall into disuse or, at best, operate inefficiently. Equally, decorators, when painting doors, have a nasty habit of painting the bolts at the same time, thus making them immovable.

CHAPTER 5
Door Locks

This chapter is to be about door locks and I would like to make my position clear. I do not consider anything to be a lock unless a key has been used in the correct operation of the piece of equipment concerned. I make this, rather obvious, point because many of the public do not agree and consider anything which keeps a door even temporarily closed to be a lock.

Before launching into the various types of lock you are most likely to encounter, I would urge some caution. There is an unfortunate misunderstanding amongst quite a large proportion of the public as to what kind of lock they have on their property. As an example, you may well be told by your client that his door is fitted with a lock manufactured by one of the largest lock manufacturers in this country, whereas that is not the case at all but the lock he has is indeed a mortise lock. The common misuse of that manufacturer's name to describe all mortise locks is quite widespread and the confusion does neither you nor that manufacturer any good, especially if the lock in question is grossly inferior. It follows that you cannot, regrettably, assume that the client means actually what he is saying. I am certain that in the main that form of description is quite innocent, but it is nevertheless real.

Do not fall into the trap of stipulating a lock which it is not practical to fit, nor stipulate a lock which is different from that already present but which does nothing to improve security. That kind of clanger dropping only serves to highlight your inexperience, which to the client and his advisers will appear as incompetence and be a black mark of considerable magnitude against you and your employer. These clangers can, of course, cost your client considerable money — locks (and fitting) are not cheap.

There is a growing tendancy amongst Insurers to have *"standard protection requirements"* which include e.g. *"all external doors must be fitted with xxxx lock"*. The idea is to bring general security standards, which are abysmally low, up to a reasonable standard. I have absolutely nothing whatsoever against that sentiment, but I have severe reservations about the method of achieving these results. Why?, you may ask, what is wrong? Well, I feel that this approach (a) goes against the theory (mine at least) that security cannot be standardised, (b) attempts to do so could, in some cases, actually result in reducing security — the lock being replaced might be better than that which it is to replace, and (c) this approach must result in a certain amount of damage being done by attempts to fit inappropriate locks to the doors concerned. I am not being insulting, or not trying to be, when I say that a large proportion of the public will not have the faintest idea what is really being talked about in these standard protection requirements, and will end up in the most horrendous pickle. It is a case of the ends trying to justify the means.

Right, now having got that off my chest, let us continue.

Mortise Locks are one of the types most commonly met, and one is illustrated in figure 20. There are, however, many makes of such locks with a consequent variety of standards. You may see many with the words *"Insurance approved"* stamped on the face plate — forget that description. As far as I can ascertain no-one in the Insurance Industry has ever been given the authority to approve security locks on behalf of the entire Insurance market.

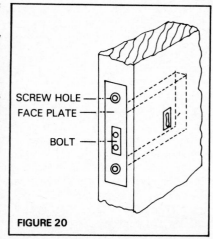

SCREW HOLE

FACE PLATE

BOLT

FIGURE 20

The mortise lock is fitted into and not onto the door, as figure 20 shows. It is obvious, therefore, that to accommodate the lock some of the door must be removed. If this leaves insufficient wood on either side of the lock then the door becomes virtually useless. Most of these locks are approximately $\frac{3}{4}$" thick so its seems reasonable not to fit this lock to a door less than $1\frac{1}{4}$" thick, which would leave $\frac{1}{4}$" wood either side of the lock. This I would consider an absolute minimum and ideally I would like to see $\frac{1}{2}$" each side of the lock. However, to achieve these minimi the lock must be fitted dead centre; if this is not done, then even the minimum thickness is not present on one side of the lock despite the overall dimensions being adequate. You must have the same kind of consideration for the depth of the lock which is an average $2\frac{3}{4}$", so the locking stile must be an absolute minimum of $3\frac{1}{2}$" deep otherwise there is insufficient wood left after the lock has been fitted. Can you imagine a locking stile $1\frac{1}{4}$" x 3" having a lock $\frac{3}{4}$" x $2\frac{3}{4}$" inserted into it? At the area of the lock there is virtually no locking stile left, i.e. a good lock surrounded by virtually nothing.

Flush doors, as described earlier, are probably the hardest to decide whether a mortise lock can be fitted or not, because the locking stile is hidden so its dimensions are unknown.

Where a lock has already been fitted in this way the situation can, to some extent, be rectified by fitting strong metal plates to the door, both sides and well secured, the plates being the full depth of the locking stile and stretching at least 6" above and below the lock. One possible snag is that the very presence of these plates could indicate to a potential burglar that the door has a weakness.

There are narrow stile mortise locks, especially designed for doors with narrow stiles where the lock depth is in the region of $2\frac{1}{4}$" (as opposed to the normal $2\frac{3}{4}$"), and these should be specified where appropriate, but you will undoubtedly find doors where even these are too large, so a mortise lock simply cannot, or at least should not, be fitted.

There are on the market *"double throw"* mortise locks where, if the key is turned through 360° twice, the bolt protrudes further than if the key is only turned through 360° once. There are points about this type of lock of which you should be aware, viz (a) a one revolution turn of the key on a double throw lock does not necessarily move the bolt the same distance as a one revolution turn of a single throw lock; it may be less, (b) people have a tendency to become lazy and, after a while, instead of turning the key twice they may only turn it once. If the distance the bolt moves is critical, possibly because of the gap between the door and frame, and the situation described in (a) above exists, then this lack of second key turn could be crucial, and (c) with some of these locks, after the second throw of the bolt there is virtually no bolt left in the lock case. Personally, I would rather see a single throw lock properly fitted than rely on the client turning the key twice, but perhaps I am over pessimistic.

You may find mortise locks fitted to metal doors, i.e. sheet metal on angle iron frame. In fact they are not being used as mortise locks but as rimlocks because they are on, and not in, the door. The only way they can be considered as being in the door is because the bolt has to pass through a hole in the angle iron frame. This is, in fact, a disadvantage because part of the bolt throw distance is negated by the thickness of the angle iron, a factor which must be taken into account when considering the lock's efficiency. The lock is usually welded onto the sheet metal and possibly part of the angle iron, which of course makes life difficult if the lock malfunctions and has to be replaced.

Just as important as the lock itself is the striking plate — see Figure 21 overleaf. There are two types, one being greatly superior to the other.

With both types of striking plate you have a metal plate with a rectangular hole, a similar size hole being cut in the locking post to a depth sufficient to receive the lock bolt. The better quality striking plate has, behind the plate hole, a metal box which then 'lines' the hole cut in the locking post, thus it is known as a 'box striking plate'. Without this box it is possible to bore a hole in the locking post and, by using a jemmy, force the bolt sufficiently far back into the lock itself to allow the door to be opened.

"Special" Mortise locks. Very thin versions of mortise locks are to be found in the rails of doors described in figure 8, these being fitted at the time of door assembly and not easily replaced without dismantling the whole door, a most costly operation — see figure 22 overleaf.

A different form of mortise lock, but still a mortise lock, is the 'clutch or claw' lock. With the normal mortise lock the bolt moves in one direction only, usually horizontally. However, if this lock were to be used on a sliding (as opposed to hinged) door, then the bolt would simply slide out of the striking plate making the lock totally ineffective. To counter this problem a claw lock is used, where the bolt moves horizontally, and having done so the end of the bolt, which has hinged sections, 'splays out' in at least two directions, the splayed portions forming hooks. Once through the hole in the striking plate these hooks are wider than the hole and therefore cannot be withdrawn unless the key is used, the key operation closing the claws before withdrawing the bolt. Obviously, the hole in the locking post, or the box in the striking plate must be larger than the hole in the striking plate, otherwise the hook will be unable to spread. This type of claw lock is a little old fashioned

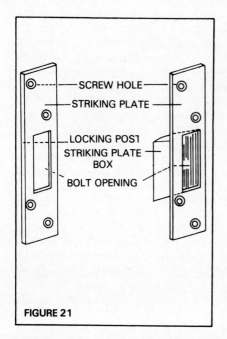

SCREW HOLE
STRIKING PLATE
LOCKING POST
STRIKING PLATE BOX
BOLT OPENING

FIGURE 21

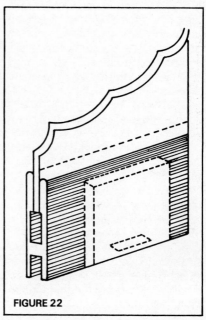

FIGURE 22

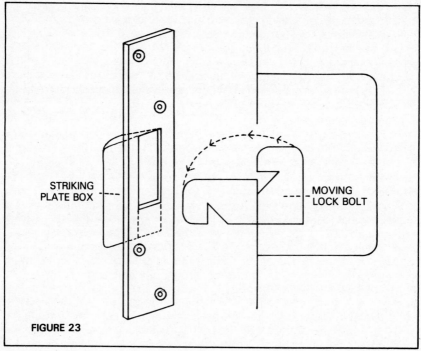

STRIKING PLATE BOX

MOVING LOCK BOLT

FIGURE 23

but is still very regularly encountered. The more recent version of this lock works on a different principle with fewer moving parts which can malfunction. With this newer type of lock the bolt does not move horizontally, but is hinged within the lock case and *'falls'* from a vertical position, through 90° to a horizontal position, a notch or hook on the bolt catching the edge of the striking plate and preventing the door from being opened, see figure 23.

Assuming the lock is of sufficient quality there is no reason why this type of lock cannot be used on a hinged door.

Another form of specialised mortise lock is that used in the modern aluminium framed door where the frame is hollow, see figure 24. As the frame is also narrow it is not possible to use the normal or even the narrow stile mortise lock. The lock used here is operated on the pin tumbler basis and the bolt is hinged to drop 90° as with the previously mentioned claw lock. Unless the correct pin tumbler mechanism is used (there are good and bad ones), the lock can easily be drilled. Because the frame is hollow aluminium it is fairly easily bent, a factor affecting the lock housing and the striking plate area which, more often than not, is just a hole cut in the locking post. If organised at the design stage it is quite possible to have strengthening metal lining in the lock area of both the locking post and stile. However, this rarely comes as standard.

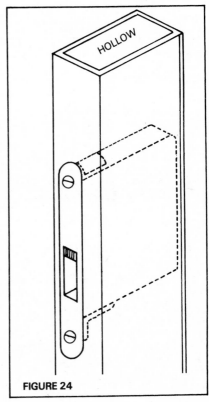

Thin metal framed glass panelled doors often have a thin mortise lock *'built in'*, but the lock is likely to be at the lower end of the security range.

Four *general* observations I would like to make are as follows:

(i) You will quite often encounter special mortise locks where, on one side of the door, instead of a keyhole there is a small handle which operates the lock bolt. Your immediate reaction should be *'this door must form part of a Fire Exit Route'*, the object of the handle being to facilitate easy egress without having to fiddle with keys in an emergency. However, having made this assumption you should verify it because it may not be the case. The handle does weaken the security as it allows easy egress to a burglar who may have gained entry by another route. If the handle is not necessary have it removed, *but* if the door is part of a Fire Exit Route *leave it,* or you may be landing someone in trouble.

FIGURE 24

33

(ii) Just because a lock is present do not assume it is used, get the keys and make sure the lock is actually operational.

(iii) Unless specific instructions are issued to the contrary, if you ask for a mortise lock (or rimlock for that matter) to be fitted, the fitter will automatically make a keyhole on both sides of the door. It is worth considering how often this is actually necessary. In the vast majority of cases, unless the door in question is a final exit door, the answer will be no! An unnecessary keyhole can serve only one purpose, viz. be an invitation to burglars or mischiefmakers to ruin a good lock by meddling with it. Apart from that it gives an unnecessary indication of the location of the lock. So if the keyhole is not needed why not have it blocked off, or better still not made in the first place!

(iv) It is amazing how much head scratching can be produced by simply asking for the use of the key. Who has it?, when was it last seen? If that is the result produced, it might raise questions about key security in general. From a security aspect the loss of the key might not be too serious if the door is actually locked and not used (get it screwed up). However, if there is another (lesser quality) lock on the door it probably indicates that the other lock will be used on its own. This all boils down to *'key security'*, and if this is bad any lock involved must be considered as poor because the key security is every bit as important as the standard of lock.

Rim Locks, sometimes known as box locks — see figure 25 — may work on the same principle as a mortise lock, but have essential differences. The mechanism within the lock casing is usually inferior both in quality and design, so there is no way most of these can be considered to be high, or even medium, security locks. The other most important feature and difference is that the lock is screwed onto the door, and not fitted into the door, so it is exposed and vulnerable. The usual method of fixing is by exposed wood screws, and the same method is used for the staple (the counterpart of the striking plate associated with mortise locks). It will be fairly obvious, therefore, that a hole in the door panel, whether it be constructed of timber or glass, sufficient to allow a hand and forearm to pass, means that if that hand holds a screwdriver the lock can be removed simply by unscrewing the screws. I know that this is not as easy as it sounds unless a large hole is made, but (a) there are skilful burglars about, and (b) who is to say the hole being made will not be large?

For some reason which I have never understood, I have yet to see non-return screws use with these locks. Whilst they would not improve the lock itself they would at least make it less easy to remove. However, if a jemmy can get through the aforementioned hole, then the lock could fairly easily be removed from the door by using brute strength. The last point is not too important however, because brute strength will overcome the majority of doors anyway, unless they have been specially strengthened.

Short of replacing this type of lock altogether, probably the best way of reducing its chances of being unscrewed, or forced, from the door (no improvement in the lock quality) is by affixing strong metal straps, specially shaped, to the door, above and below and going over the lock, these straps being held onto the door by coach bolts with the domed heads on the outside, and the nuts (internal) defaced to prevent unbolting through the aforementioned holes.

Once again, non-return screws can be used but are easier to force off the door than coach bolts, especially as when the door ages the screws work loose normally. It is obvious that if these metal straps are being fitted over the lock, a similar strap must be fitted over the staple, and similarly fixed.

You will find these locks on many old doors which are capable of taking mortise locks, but which had the rim locks fitted when they were more fashionable. Other situations are (a) when the door frame is too thin to take a mortise lock, and (b) where a *'cheap job'* has been carried out.

Generally, not a lock to be recommended.

Cylinder Rim Latch which, if not properly described in a report, can be confused with the Rim Lock aforementioned. These come in varying standards from low and easy to overcome (see figure 26), to the more sophisticated (see figure 27).

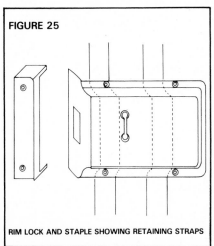

FIGURE 25

RIM LOCK AND STAPLE SHOWING RETAINING STRAPS

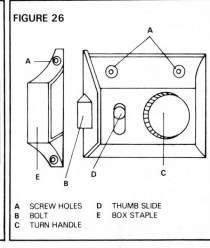

FIGURE 26

A	SCREW HOLES	D	THUMB SLIDE
B	BOLT	E	BOX STAPLE
C	TURN HANDLE		

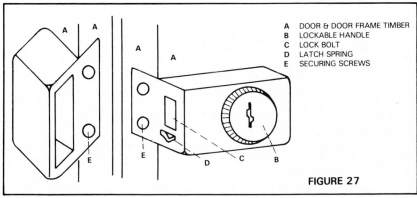

A	DOOR & DOOR FRAME TIMBER
B	LOCKABLE HANDLE
C	LOCK BOLT
D	LATCH SPRING
E	SECURING SCREWS

FIGURE 27

The cheaper versions suffer from one of the Rim Lock's problems i.e. they are affixed to the door surface with exposed screws. However, because the lock is comparatively small and the operating features close together it cannot have strengthening straps fitted. I do not, at this stage, want to go into the operating mechanism too closely as this will be mentioned later in this book. However, it has to be mentioned at this point that the bolt is not deadlocking i.e. it can easily (and intentionally) be forced back into the lock housing, this being an essential feature for the *'slam action'* for which it is used. Because the bolt is bevelled it is, in many cases, nht too difficult to foature for the *'slam action'* for which it is used. Because the bolt is bevelled it is, in many cases, not too difficult to force the bolt back from outside the door, thus gaining entry. Some of these locks have a *'slide'* which is finger operated from inside the door; this slide is intended to deadlock the bolt so that it cannot be manipulated illegally, There are two snags to this slide, (a) they are simply not reliable and (b) it is very often when the slide is in the *'down'* position that deadlocking occurs, so when the lock ages and components become loose this slide can accidentally operate when the door is slammed thus locking out the keyholder, as even the use of the key will not overcome the slide *'locking'*. Having said that the slide is unreliable you can bet it is under circumstances mentioned in (b) that the slide will choose to work. Apart from the slide there is no way the lock can be locked from the inside.

The more expensive, and more secure, versions have the securing screws for both the lock and staple on the edge so that when the door is locked the screws are hidden and not so vulnerable. This lock can also be locked by use of the key both internally and externally. The bolt is rectangular and not bevelled as in the cheaper variety, the slam action being triggered by a separate *'latch spring'* beneath the bolt; where this is present the lock is actually deadlocking and cannot easily be pushed back.

The cheaper version is not a good lock but the better versions are reasonable and the top end of the good locks are very good.

These locks are found on doors which are too thin to take mortise locks and also on the majority of house front doors.

Mortise Rack Bolts or Door Security Bolts — see figure 28 — although small, should still, in my opinion be considered locks if for no other reason than that they are *'key'* operated. Mind you, the keys are simple and have little variation so that one key will fit many locks. The bolt is moved out of its housing by twisting the key through quite a few revolutions, operating a small ratchet mechanism which moves the bolt. The length of throw is not great and the bolt *'receptacle'* is usually a hole in the door frame with a thin metal plate over. All things considered this is not a strong piece of equipment, but its addition to a door with other locks already fitted adds some, if not much, strength. If they are added to a door with an existing lock and hinge bolts, there are several points of *'securing'* thus making it harder to overcome.

Padlocks — Generally speaking these fall into two broad categories, viz. open and closed shackle, these being illustrated in figures 29 and 30. The shackle is the *'hoop'* through which the object to be locked is passed. The larger the area of the loop the more open shackled the padlock is considered to be. Unless the object passing through the shackle virtually fills the space, it follows that there will be sufficient space left over for the insertion of a jemmy or other suitable implement. You will, therefore, have deduced that in most cases a close shackle padlock is best. However, the size of the shackle is only one point of importance; the case strength, construction, the shackle strength, the joint strength etc. are equally important, with the result that within the two categories i.e. closed or open, there are large variations in quality. As it is not my object to compare various products, I suggest the reader consults a more experienced surveyor for guidance on individual locks. Suffice it to say that there is a tremendous variety, and just because a lock looks strong, it need not necessarily be so.

Locking Bars — Although the majority of these contain no locking mechanism themselves, they are, for decent security, an essential adjunct to the padlocks mentioned above. Examples of typical locking bars, which are made from strong, thick metal, are shown in figures 31, 32 and 33.

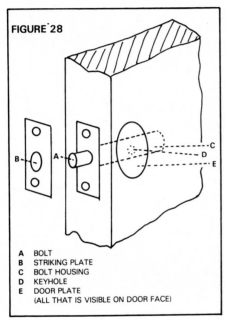

FIGURE 28

A BOLT
B STRIKING PLATE
C BOLT HOUSING
D KEYHOLE
E DOOR PLATE
   (ALL THAT IS VISIBLE ON DOOR FACE)

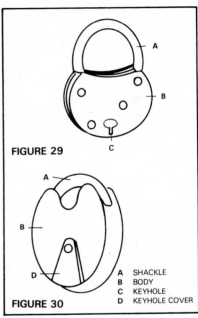

FIGURE 29

FIGURE 30

A SHACKLE
B BODY
C KEYHOLE
D KEYHOLE COVER

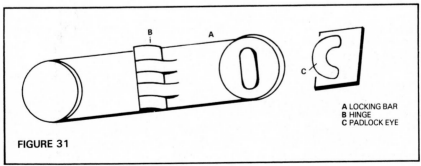

A LOCKING BAR
B HINGE
C PADLOCK EYE

FIGURE 31

The part containing the padlock eye is fitted to either the door frame or the first closing leaf of a double leaf door, and the other part is fixed to the door itself or the final closing leaf. These locking bars are anything but cheap (neither are decent padlocks) so it only makes sense to have them fitted with coach bolts, as to do otherwise would be a complete waste of money and would negate the otherwise good security provided.

In more recent years locking bars have been developed which do not use padlocks as they have a locking mechanism as an integral, hidden part — see figure 34. There is little doubt that the majority of this type of locking bar is good, but my experience is that the engineering is so fine that unless the two sections marry up virtually perfectly then operation of the locking mechanism is almost impossible. Bearing this in mind, try and visualise the problems of locking a large double leaf door on a dark, stormy, rainy winter night; it must be virtually impossible. This might account for the fact that these locks are not selling in large numbers. Remember, it is not good security to recommend a piece of equipment that may not be used because it is difficult to handle.

By no means comparable in security terms, but unfortunately often used with 'security' in mind are what I call garden shed fitments. These are very weak open shackle padlocks used with a hasp as illustrated in figure 35. The hasp is so weak and the fixing holes so small that only wood screws can be used, so virtually all the components can be easily broken. Unfortunately, in common with other devices, you may well encounter these pieces of equipment used to secure external doors to buildings and I can see no possible excuse for accepting them as suitable.

Locking Brackets — These are illustrated in figure 36, and are not, in my opinion, used as often as they should be. Their prime, but not sole, use is with double leaf sliding timber or metal doors. The brackets are screwed or coach bolted to the side of the door opposite to that which is to have the padlock. The bracket then passes along the edge of the door and protrudes out from the other side. The two brackets are drawn together and padlocked. Once again, to be effective the bracket metal must be strong and should not protrude further than is necessary to expose the hole for the padlock, and a close shackle padlock should be used.

Cross Bars — These are metal bars, used internally to secure doors and, at the same time, afford some physical reinforcement to the door itself. There are many ways these bars, which should be approx 2½" x ⅜", are fitted, varying from (a) resting in U brackets, (b) fitting into slots cut in adjoining masonry, to (c) padlocked to the door or door surround. I prefer (c) where an example would be as follows. The bar fits into two metal holders which are coach bolted or screwed onto the doorframe. An 'eye' welded onto the centre of the bar engages over a 'tongue' fitted to the door itself and the two are padlocked together. The 'eye' and 'tongue' are similar to the two parts of a locking bar as described earlier. By using this method, as opposed to (a) and (b) above, it eradicates the possibility of (1) removing the bar (from outside) by use of knives and the like (2) masonry holes 'wearing' so that they become useless (3) shaking loose if the bar is not left in a central position (4) easy removal if entry is gained by some other route. An example of the lockable type is illustrated in figure 37.

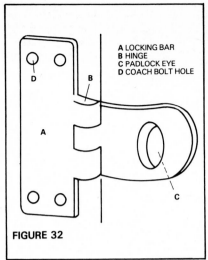

A LOCKING BAR
B HINGE
C PADLOCK EYE
D COACH BOLT HOLE

FIGURE 32

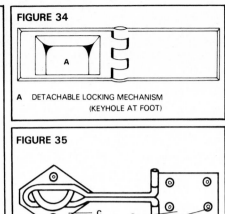

FIGURE 34

A   DETACHABLE LOCKING MECHANISM
(KEYHOLE AT FOOT)

FIGURE 35

A   SCREW HOLES   B   HASP   C   STAPLE

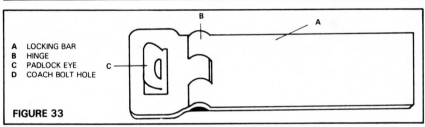

A   LOCKING BAR
B   HINGE
C   PADLOCK EYE
D   COACH BOLT HOLE

FIGURE 33

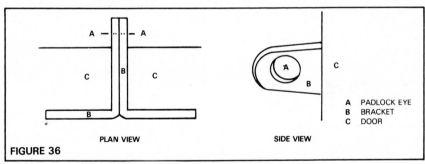

PLAN VIEW   SIDE VIEW

A   PADLOCK EYE
B   BRACKET
C   DOOR

FIGURE 36

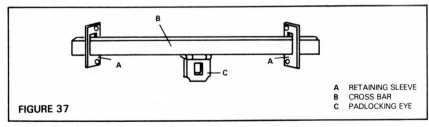

A   RETAINING SLEEVE
B   CROSS BAR
C   PADLOCKING EYE

FIGURE 37

CHAPTER 6

Lock Mechanisms

In the previous chapter we were looking at locks and their application to varying types of doors. At that time very little detail of how locks operated was mentioned and now mechanisms will be described in very basic terms bearing in mind the intended readership. Anyone wishing to delve deeper into the subject can find plenty of literature, if necessary by reference to the principal manufacturers.

The Mortise Lock is probably the most recommended and accepted in insurance circles and by the public. The lock fits into the door itself and, if properly installed, only sufficient timber will have been removed from the door to permit a tight fit for the lock. Excess removal of timber only leads to unnecessary weakening of the door.

The lock bolt has to engage in a receiving point in the locking post and this should be a *'boxed striking plate'* as indicated in figure 38. Unfortunately, you will all too often encounter cases where the receiving point is nothing but a hole cut in the timber of the locking post whilst, in other cases, the hole will have a facing plate (striking plate) but no *box*. It is completely false economy and poor security, often performed by the DIY person or the cowboy installer, to have a good lock and a poor striking plate.

Let us know consider, in basic terms, the operations necessary to move the locking bolt to secure the door.

Within the lock case there are fixed and moving parts and it is only when all of these component parts are in a specific position relative to each other that a key will be able to move the lock bolt. This sounds fairly simple and, in a low quality lock, it is. But if it were as simple as that two very important features would occur viz. (1) It would not be too difficult to make a key to operate the lock *'illegally'*, (2) The locks would be basically very similar and, therefore, one key could operate many locks making security nil. The good lock manufacturer has made matters more complicated, and therefore the locks more individualistic and secure, by having the moving parts within each lock differently shaped and/or positioned from the overwhelming majority of other locks they manufacture. A very large proportion of mortise locks have as their most important moving parts *'levers'*, these being thin sheets of metal as illustrated in figure 39. When in a dormant condition the lever is held in place by a spring, but when the correct key is used the lever is moved and the bolt stump (fixed to the bolt itself) is free to pass a specifically shaped *'cut out'*. By adding more levers with slightly differing shapes, and by producing a correspondingly shaped key, it will be seen that the security improves because more variation in the combination of shapes etc. is available.

However, the size, or lack of it, of the lock case does place restrictions on the number of moving parts which can be accommodated. To enlarge the lock case to take more moving parts just results in a weaker door, as more timber must be removed to take a larger lock case. A lock which is designed to be operated from both sides of the door has to be symmetrical, thus restricting the number of permutations available. Conversely, a lock which needs only to be operated from one side of the door does not have this requirement and many more combinations or 'differs' would be available. However, although there are many cases where such a lock would be the most appropriate, how often do you come across one, other than on safe and strongroom doors?

So far we have considered variations within the lock mechanism, but key construction can be varied in many ways to provide further differences. However, if a key is available for examination it is possible, provided the correct equipment and ability is present, to create a duplicate key. For that reason the key differences, although important, cannot really be considered as security features. We will consider the key briefly, if for no other reason than that you will often encounter locks which are not marked with the number of levers.

It is often thought that by examining a key you can tell the number of levers in a lock, but this does not always follow. You must always remember that the key must be symmetrical for operation from either side of the door. If you look at figure 40 you will see five projections from the key. One projection is always used for moving the lock bolt, leaving four. However, you must ask

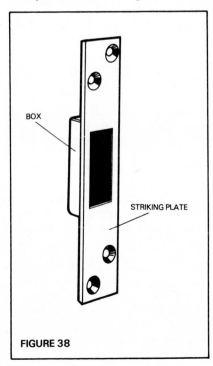

FIGURE 38

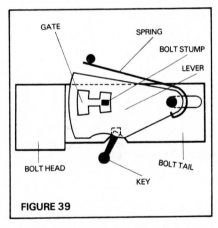

FIGURE 39

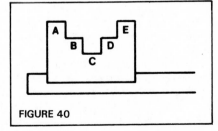

FIGURE 40

yourself if these four all operate levers or if one of them is spare in one direction and the bolt mover in the other? In fact this is a typical key for a four lever lock, but it could be for a three lever lock with one projection 'free'. If you now refer to figure 41 you will see an illustration of the key to a typical 5 lever lock which has the spare projection, but a six lever lock key will look the same. You will see, therefore, that you cannot ascertain a lock's degree of security just by looking at the key, although you may get a rough indication.

The bolt which passes from the lock into the striking plate in the locking post obviously passes through a gap i.e. the space between the door and the doorframe. It is not possible for there to be no gap at all otherwise the door would be so 'tight' that it could not be opened or closed. However, the size of the gap can vary, but if it is excessive then the door should be replaced. The bolt, whilst in this 'gap', is liable to attack it could be hacksawed. To counter this, good quality locks have, within the bolt, hardened steel inserts or laminations which are visible if you look at the bolt end. In some cases these inserts can rotate so that the hacksaw blade is ineffective.

Probably the next most common key mechanism, after that mentioned above, is the **'pin tumbler'** type (see figure 42). The main body of the lock contains a circular barrel capable of revolving. There are holes in the lock body and also in the barrel, the holes in the two parts matching exactly. Small metal pins are inserted in the aligned holes but they are not the full length of any 'pair' of holes, as the holes also contain a small spring. A correct key inserted in the keyway pushes the bottom pins against the top pins and, in turn, against the springs. Where the bottom and top pins 'touch' there is a hairline gap and when all of these hairline gaps are in exact line with the separation between the barrel and lockcase it allows the barrel to rotate and move the lock bolt. One would think, initially, all one had to do was to raise all the bottom pins the same distance to achieve the correct result, but this is not the case. The lower pins are of varying length so, unless each and every one of them is raised to the exact height required, the lock will not operate properly. This is the reason for the shape of the key as illustrated in figure 43. You will see that grooves are also cut along the length of both sides of the key and these must align with obstacles at the mouth of the keyway as indicated in figure 44.

As well as moving bolts similar to the 'lever' lock, you will often find the pin tumbler type lock moving the bolt through 90° outwards from the door edge (semaphore action). The actual bolt can be one solid piece of metal but very often it is several layers of metal laminated together. With the lever type lock the boxed striking plate prevents the bolt being forced back into the lock case. However, with the 90° moving bolt only some have a defence against this forcing action. Consequently, it is even more important than ever that the gap between door and door frame is as small as possible or, alternatively, physically shielded.

The two types of mechanism so far described are the main ones you will encounter, but there are others which are variations on these principles using alternative designs and components with the same objectives; the keys are also different but objectively the same. To go into greater detail would involve advertising which is not the intention of this book.

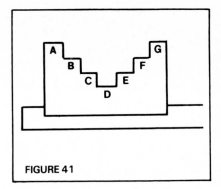

FIGURE 41

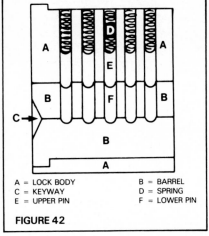

A = LOCK BODY   B = BARREL
C = KEYWAY   D = SPRING
E = UPPER PIN   F = LOWER PIN

FIGURE 42

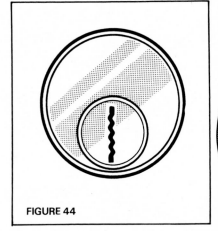

FIGURE 44

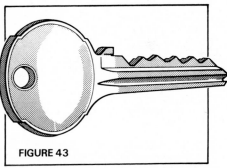

FIGURE 43

Box rimlocks work on the same principle as the aforementioned lever type locks, but usually the mechanism within the lock case is simple and not of the high security grading. The weakness of the rim fitting has been described earlier.

Rimlatches, as mentioned earlier, have a fairly wide range of security grading depending upon the manufacturer and the design. They can be either deadlocking, i.e. the bolt can only be moved (legally) by operation of the key, or alternatively the bolt can be *'sprung'* and wedged to have a *'slam action'*. This bolt can be depressed by the finger unless additional locking devices are incorporated in the mechanism.

The actual locking mechanism is usually the *'pin tumbler'* variety as previously described, or a variation thereof. In the higher grade locks the bolt can be deadlocked by additional turns of the key or by snibs which interfere with the spring action. Once again, I would refer you to the earlier chapter which described the advantages and disadvantages of the fitting methods.

Padlocks can have either of the two types of locking mechanism as previously described. Those with lever actions usually have the keyhole in the face of the body whilst those having the pin tumbler mechanism have the keyhole in the bottom of the lock body. If you try to visualise the variety of sizes of padlock and try to imagine the space available within the body for moving parts etc., you can readily accept, I hope, that it is virtually impossible to have a complex locking mechanism in the very small examples. It does not, however, follow that because a padlock is large the mechanism within is complex and secure. You must refer to the manufacturer's sales description and any other technical information you can assimilate to assess the degree of security.

Key security — You can have the best lock in the world but if the key control is lacking then the entire security is absolutely useless. On many visits you make to premises you will find the keys left in the lock. If you challenge a client on the wisdom of this there will almost always be a plausible answer ready. If you are as sceptical as I am, you will probably discount these answers and accept that the client is either lazy or badly organised. You are then faced with the problem of convincing the client of the folly of his ways, not only from the point of view of making things easy for the burglar, but also pointing out that this action may well invalidate an insurance claim should a loss by use of keys occur!

Keys should never be in a lock unless the lock is actually being used, but that does not mean they can be left around anywhere for potential intruders or collaborators to steal or copy. They should always be in someone's possession, or if too numerous to carry about they should be locked in a safe place which, in turn, should be locked. There is often a tendency to have a large number of keys made so that several members of staff can have one. Whilst there are many cases where this is necessary because of irregular comings and goings of staff, there are also many instances where it is totally unnecessary. Wherever possible this practice should be discouraged and the number of keys per lock kept to a minimum. The more keys there are the more likelihood there is of one being lost. If this does occur the only real answer is to have the lock changed, as to take a chance that whoever finds the key will not know which lock it fits is exactly that, *'taking a chance'*, and security should never be left to chance.

I wonder how many, or how few, surveyors actually give their clients advice on key security — not many I would suggest.

I have intentionally not mentioned master key systems as I do not think they are likely to come within the orbit of novice surveyors.

CHAPTER 7
Doors — Physical Protection

In previous chapters we have described the door structure, we have hung and fitted the door (and tried to prevent vehicles demolishing them), and have locked the door.

Without progressing to Intruder Alarms (which will be dealt with later) we have to protect the actual door itself. Quite often that is the means of entry, but not by the more skilful manipulation of locks or overcoming fittings. Strengthening of the door is usually achieved by adding something to it which is not there in the basic design.

All of the following additions to the door obviously increase its weight , therefore the hinges etc have all to be re-assessed. Purely as an example, metal sheeting (which will be explained very shortly) weighs approximately $2\frac{1}{2}$ lbs per square foot, and a door of 6'3" x 2'9" (fairly average) will have in the region of 43 lbs weight added. It cannot be taken for granted that heavier or stronger hinges can easily be fitted as there may not be sufficient space on the hanging post for the longer hinges. You may have to ask for additional, not longer, hinges. As mentioned previously, hinge bolts do not solve this problem because they are not *'working'* when the door is open.

A   **Metal facing/lining.** That very expression causes much controversy, the arguments for the metal being placed on the inside (lining) or outside (facing) of the door being quite numerous. Some people say that the metal outside provides a deterrent, others say that if it is on the inside burglars may not come prepared, thinking they have only a timber door to face. I am not going to fall into the trap of making a ruling as to which argument is correct, but I do confess to preferring the facing wherever practicable.

Regardless of which method is used, one thing is certain; purchasing and applying suitable metal is not cheap. The obvious result is that you will often encounter *'cheap jobs'* which are virtually useless.

Before we proceed into the metal and its fixings we must consider the reasons for using the facing (or lining). The obvious first reason is purely because the door structure is not sufficiently strong for the situation in which it is encountered. The other reasons will probably include the situation where the door is considered to be especially vulnerable to attack, or especially secluded. However, one reason often used, in my opinion wrongly, is that the basic door is deteriorating and the metal is used as a form of reinforcement. I see no sense in this as such door deterioration is probably going to result in the metal falling off or at least coming loose. Neither do I think sheet metal is suitable for glass panelled doors where the glass forms more than 25% of the door surface, my reasoning being that there would be insufficient fixing points.

Let us assume, therefore, that the basic door is adequate and that metal facing is a practical proposition.

Because the expense involved is considerable, you should, in my opinion, be quite specific about your requirements otherwise you may be a cause of the client wasting his money and, equally importantly, bringing your profession into disrepute. Being specific means that you must think the whole situation through, and not just give a stereotyped prescription.

The metal to be used should be at least 14 gauge (0.080" or 2.0mm) in thickness.

If you ask for the metal facing to cover the entire door surface it will probably mean that, unless the door was loose fitting beforehand, the addition of the metal will result in the door not closing properly as it will jam between the door and the door stop. If the door stop is just nailed on then it may be a simple job to reposition it. However, if it is an integral part of the hinge and locking posts then these will have to be trimmed by a carpenter to provide sufficient space for the metal to fit; not as easy as it sounds. If you go even further with your specification and ask for the metal to be wrapped around the door edges, then for the same reason, viz. lack of space to accommodate the metal, the door must be trimmed around all edges. Not only that, the hinges have to be removed and refitted, holes having to be made in the metal to cope with them. All of that is time consuming and therefore even more costly. Remember, assuming a $2\frac{1}{2}''$ thick door (6'3" x 2'9") the additional weight of the 'wrapped around metal' is in the region of 10 lb. You will see, I hope, from the foregoing that great thought is required before you specify. Unless the risk or potential problem is extreme, I prefer to ask for the metal to cover 'the exposed face of the door when it is closed'. The exception to this is where the door stop is just 'nailed on', because this can usually be easily removed. In these circumstances the metal should cover 'the exposed face of the door when it is open', (including that portion hidden by the door stop) and the door stops should be repositioned. This latter proviso also applies when the door is outward opening, as the door stops are then internal and not affected.

If you are having the door metal lined then depending on whether the door opens in or out you should consider the same potential problems.

The metal, to be effective, must be well secured to the door, and I suggest that coach bolts at 6" intervals should be used along the door stiles and rails, hence the limitation in the area of glass permissible. You will encounter situations where the presence, internally, of the nuts securing the bolts will be considered too unsightly to be acceptable. In such cases you have little option but to accept non-return screws at 4" intervals, but you must insist upon the screwholes in the metal sheet being countersunk to prevent the screw heads standing proud. I can think of no circumstances where ordinary slotted wood screws should be considered acceptable, although sometimes this is done and then the heads of the screws are defaced to prevent removal. Unfortunately, you will rarely find the aforementioned fixing points adhered to, the spacings usually being much greater. Inferior metal and fixing methods to those mentioned above should not, in my opinion, be considered *'security'*, only a cover up job.

B   **Timber lining** — A much lesser degree of security, but slightly better than none at all, can be achieved by lining the door with plywood or chipboard at least $\frac{3}{8}$" thick, bolted or screwed in a similar way to that mentioned in 'A' above. I have not suggested this timber be used as a facing as, if the door is external, then weathering is likely to cause severe deterioration in a comparatively short space of time.

It is obvious that timber cannot be wrapped around the door edges, nor (because of the thickness involved) can it be inserted between the door and the door stop.

C   **Metal Mesh lining** — Metal mesh, assuming the mesh is small and all intersections are welded, can be used as a lining, but I have not come across it very often. The fixing method and spacings should be as for (A) above but, in addition to the internal nuts, washers may also be necessary. You may find this mesh secured by ordinary screws with washers, but I doubt if it has anywhere near the same strength.

I do not recommend this form of protection externally as it could be comparatively easy to remove if a chain can be threaded through the mesh and attached to a vehicle.

D   **Metal Grilles** — These consist of wire, ideally not less than 10 gauge (0.128" or 3.25mm), woven into mesh of either diamond or square pattern, preferably with each intersection spot welded. The squares should not be greater than 1" x 1" (or smaller if glass breakage is also being considered) to prevent an arm being extended through the holes. The mesh must then be fixed to a frame, preferably angle iron which, in turn, must be fixed to the door itself.

If the grille is being fitted externally it will probably be secured by the use of padlocks. A bracket will be permanently fixed to the door in a manner which is difficult to remove, i.e. non return screws or the screws obscured by the grille frame. Similar brackets must be affixed to the grille frame (usually by welding) and each of the brackets must have holes of sufficient size to allow decent padlocks to be used. You will doubtless encounter many occasions where good grilles (and costly too) are completely wasted by holes which are so small that only small, weak, useless padlocks can be used. Far fetched? Don't you believe it, it is only too common!

If the grille is to be fitted to the inside of the door then the fixings are sometimes as for outside, but more often it is just screwed to the door frame in some manner. I do not like to see the frame screwed directly onto the door frame, because this means every time the grille is removed (for cleaning etc.), either longer screws have to be used or new holes made, throwing the grille away from its original siting. It is preferable to treat the grille as if it was going to be removed daily, even if this is not done, and the fixings etc. applied accordingly.

I have come across, with increasing frequency recently, "external metal mesh gates". They are similar to the above, but not attached to the door itself. There is a gap, usually about 6", between the door and the gate, the gate being affixed to the brickwork etc with hinges and secured, when closed, by a padlock. They are, in effect, secondary doors and not in replacement for anything. One purpose is so that the solid door can be left open during business hours for ventilation, the gate keeping out intruders and preventing "back door pilfering". These gates must never be used where the door concerned forms part of a Fire Exit Route. One drawback to the security value of these gates is the aforementioned gap between the door and the gate. It enables chains and the like to be fed through the metal mesh, and if the chain is then attached to a vehicle the gate can be ripped from its fixings.

E   **Metal Bars** — I feel strongly that these should always be fitted internally as they are too liable to attack if external. This may appear a strange argument, having previously opted for sheet metal to be fitted externally. My logic is that when properly fitted the sheet metal will be in contact with the door at all points. However, it is virtually impossible to achieve this with bars, and the space between the bars and the door can be vital for the insertion of implements for bar removal or cutting.

Bars should be either solid round iron not less than $\frac{5}{8}$" in diameter, solid square iron not less than $\frac{5}{8}$" in section, or solid flat iron not less than 1" in width and $\frac{3}{8}$" in thickness.

The bars should be affixed to the door by coach bolts (thus necessitating the round bars having flattened ends), with the nuts on the inside. Ordinary wood screws should not be used, because if a hole is made in the door, and considerable force applied to the bars, it is quite conceivable for the screws to be forced out of the door. If ordinary screws have been used in a situation where the bars have been installed before you arrive, the situation can be improved by having flat metal straps put across the screw heads, the straps being secured to the door by coach bolts.

The bar spacings should not be in excess of 4" and, if fitted vertically, tie bars should be fitted at 2'6" intervals, these tie bars being similarly secured to the door.

CHAPTER 8
Windows — construction and fittings

I feel that we have dealt fairly extensively with doors and their physical attachments. Let us now turn to windows. In the average premises (I know there are exceptions) there will be more windows than any other legal opening, and within that same premises you are likely to meet a considerable array of types. It appears to be the trend in modern buildings that all windows are very similar, but that did not appear to be the case in days gone by. Also, older buildings are likely to have their window styling changed by a variety of occupants, all with differing desires and requirements.

Regardless of the type of window involved, and equally important as the type and construction, is its location. Two identical windows in completely differing positions within the same building can present totally different problems. Whether or not the window is accessible to a would be burglar is of paramount importance. Even this factor can vary depending upon what is within the building because greater potential reward will bring forth burglars (a) with more equipment to scale heights etc., and (b) more prepared to take chances you and I might consider horrific. You must, therefore, when considering windows, look for height, parapets, drain pipes (plastic ones are not as strong as the older metal type), walls, fire escapes etc., all of which are a godsend to the burglar.

The type of glass is just as important as the window design, if for no other reason than the heavier types of glass are not really suitable for windows which open. The most commonly met types of glass have been described earlier under timber and metal framed glass panelled doors. Any glass you meet in doors you are also likely to encounter in windows. One additional type, comparatively new but growing in use, is laminated glass. It is probably the strongest type on the market and is, in effect, a series of glass sheets bonded together with layers of plastic laminates, the plastic giving additional strength to the window, this product sometimes being known as *'bandit glass'*. Depending upon the risk behind the window concerned, the layers can be built up to provide finished windows well in excess of 3" thickness, but such windows are both extremely heavy and extremely costly. One further point on glass which is not really a burglary problem, but is very relevant for insurance of the glass breakage risk. If the glass has a "non standard finish" eg reeded, or is abnormally shaped or inscribed etc, this should be reported specifically in detail to any underwriter involved as it will almost certainly attract an additional premium due to its high replacement costs.

Let us now consider the actual designs of window you are most likely to come across.

A. **Fixed** — This type is probably the most common and is found in combination with opening types as well as on its own. Normal sheet, wired or leaded glass is usually found in metal or timber frames, kept in place by grooves, beading or window putty. Presumably for appearances sake, the putty is invariably on the outside of the window, subject to weathering and general wear and tear resulting in its decay and easy removal by Burglar Bill.

    The heavier and stronger glasses are often found with side edges exposed (which at least gives you a chance to measure the thickness), or cemented and clipped (with metal brackets) to adjoining panes. Some Insurers charge extra premium for this latter method of securing.

    One very important factor which must be borne in mind with heavier glasses is that the strength of the frame and the stallriser must be adequate; the weight of a large sheet of armoured plate or laminated glass is quite amazing.

B. **Sash** — see figures 45 and 46. The majority of this type of window you will encounter will be timber framed, but recently there has been a considerable increase in those having lightweight metal frames. I would expect that with the increased availability of these lightweight metals this growth will continue, although personally I have not yet encountered them. I would also think plastic frames for this style of window will arrive sooner or later. Figure 46 shows that invariably the topmost section is also the outermost one. In some cases only one section moves but more commonly they both move in a vertical plane. Each section is held in place by runners of the same material as the window frame. Where these runners are timber they are often quite flimsy and not difficult to break intentionally or accidentally, and if that happens it is easy to completely remove the runner without much effort, thus making the window

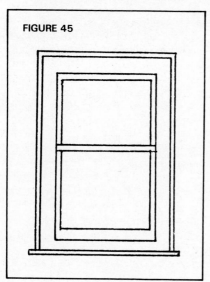

FIGURE 45

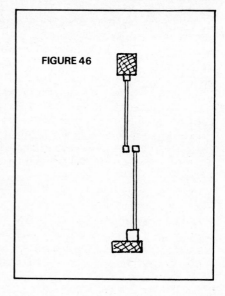

FIGURE 46

50

moveable on a horizontal plane and no "security" will have been inbuilt for that type of movement. Where the premises are quite old the frames have often been painted (poorly) so often that the sections cannot be moved; that is until Bill Burglar comes along and he always seems to have more strength than Joe Public, so I leave it to you to decide whether excessive painting is considered *'security'*. I certainly don't, but you will face many an argument over this, usually from clients.

C. **Casement** — see figures 47, 48 and 49. These figures show side hinged opening sections which are the most common, but you will come across others which are centre hinged (actually pivoted) with the opening being on a vertical or horizontal plane. In these latter types part of the opening section moves in and part out of the room concerned. Variations on all of these hinge (or pivot) positionings exist and you will have to treat them as you find them. These windows are available in timber, metal or plastic frames.

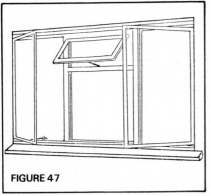

FIGURE 47

D. **Fanlights** — These are comparatively small areas of glass found above doors and fixed windows and as an integral part of casement windows. These fanlights can be fixed, top hinged, bottom hinged or centre hinged, there being no apparent ruling about how the combinations are formed. Top hinged fanlights invariably open outwards and bottom hinged open inwards, but doubtless you will encounter cases which contradict the norm.

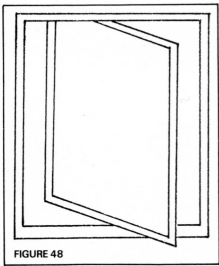

FIGURE 48

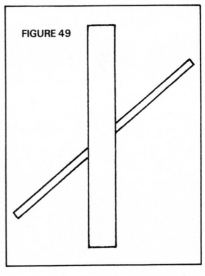

FIGURE 49

The fanlights also come in timber, metal and plastic frames.

Probably the most troublesome type of fanlight from a security point of view is the louvred type. These are broad, fairly thin, pieces of glass held in thin metal or plastic frames which are centre hinged, either vertically or horizontally, by means of a mechanism operated by a projecting handle. When one louvre is opened then all within that section are similarly opened. The number of louvres in a section varies from one upwards, and depending upon the opening you can have more than one section. The major problem with louvres is that the frame holding each pane of glass is very thin and weak, with the result that it is very easy to prise the frame away from the glass and remove the glass noiselessly, almost the same problem as with leaded glass and its fixings as mentioned earlier.

E. **Sliding** windows are almost always metal framed and look almost like sash windows turned through 90°. Similarly, you can have windows where all sections move, or others where some are fixed permanently. Probably one of the greatest problems with this type of window is that a very large proportion of them have exceedingly narrow frames, making lock fitting very difficult and, in some extreme cases, actually impossible.

Another form of sliding window, or so it is often considered, is really a door, viz. the patio door. A comparatively recent development, growing with the use of aluminium and also of double glazing, there has been an enormous growth in the number of these doors and they are encountered mainly, but by no means exclusively, in private dwellings. The normal design is to have a large fixed double glazed unit, and a similar size and construction sliding unit adjoining, although in some cases both units slide. It is literally the weight of the sliding unit which keeps it within its runners. If the unit can be lifted, and a garden spade is a favourite implement, then it can be completely removed and a large entry hole gained. It would certainly take more than one person to do this, but burglars have been known to work in two's and three's, so unless properly secured this can be, and is, a ready means of access.

General

I think at this stage it might be advantageous to re-read Chapter 3, which dealt with the various types of glass found in doors and the importance of frames and separations between the different panes of glass. All of the problems mentioned in that Chapter apply equally to windows.

SECURING DEVICES

Before proceeding too far I think it is important to remind readers of one point, which may appear obvious but which I feel is often overlooked, or at least misunderstood. Securing devices and locks cannot prevent burglars making an entry, at best they secure the window frame and do nothing to the glass itself.

This section has been headed securing devices and it should not be confused with locks. In my opinion the distinction is quite clear, viz. securing devices do not have keys (although some may have permanently attached a screw for tightening them into position), whereas locks do. The vital point being the ease with which a securing device can be operated from outside the building as opposed to a lock, assuming that a lock is being properly used and not, for instance, left with the key in it.

Most, if not all, windows are supplied with securing devices fitted, but the majority are fairly primitive, obvious and easily overcome. Those which are operated by finger movement only can obviously be *'undone'* by anyone who makes a hole in the glass of sufficient size for a hand to be inserted.

Let us now look at some of these securing devices, although I have no doubt you will meet others not mentioned here.

Sash Window

(i)   Sash fastener — see figure 50. The portion with the hinged arm is fitted to the top (outermost) section and the portion with the retaining bracket is fitted to the bottom (innermost) section. When the window is closed the fastener is as indicated in figure 50, but when open the arm is swung round so that it lies over its own base plate. When closed the arm bridges a gap between the two window sections and a knife inserted in the gap can move the arm to the open position.

(ii) Fitch — see figure 51. This is considered, if in good condition, to be better than the sash fastener although it operates on the same basic principle. However, instead of an arm there is a thickish metal plate which is bevelled and moves on a central *'pivot'*, and when closed wedges (if in good condition quite tightly) into the receiving section. In this case the moving section is on the lower leaf of the window, and although it too bridges a gap between the two window sections its shape, and the fact it has to move in a circular direction, means it is much harder to move by any knife etc. inserted into the air gap.

(iii) Hinged screw — see figure 52. A hinged, threaded screw is attached to the

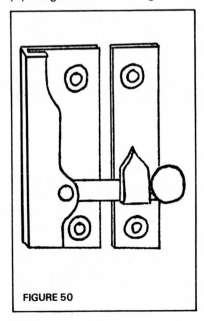

FIGURE 50

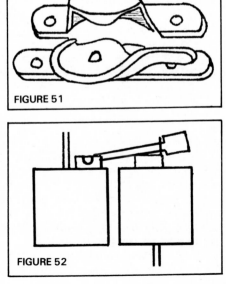

FIGURE 51

FIGURE 52

outermost window section, and when closed the screw moves down over a bracket fixed onto the other window section, then a nut is twisted down the screw to tighten the two sections together. Once again, the afore-mentioned air gap is bridged, and if the nut is not tightened sufficiently a knife, properly inserted, could push the screw out of its fixing bracket.

I have heard of instances where the threaded screw has, when the window is open, fallen forward. The result is that when an attempt is made to close the window, the upward (but not vertical) pointing screw hits the framework of the other window section. The result can be one or any of four, viz (i) the framework of the window is damaged, (ii) the screw is damaged, (iii) the window is never again properly closed, or (iv) the glass is broken.

If at ground level (or onto a balcony) it is fairly easy, but inconvenient, to go outside and, with a knife, push the screw to the vertical position and close the window, but this is not recommended when many floors above ground level. I suppose "fishing" with wire coathangers could also retrieve the screw to its vertical position, but all that trouble is more likely to lead to lack of proper use.

(iv) Sash screw — see figure 53. This is just a long screw with a flattened head (for finger use) which screws through a hole drilled through the innermost window section and into a hole drilled in (but not through) the outermost section.

(v) Acorn Stop — see figure 54. This is a small thick screw which fits into a hole in the topmost window section, usually about 3" from the foot, on the side frame. The screw protrudes out from the window, thus permitting a 3" movement of either of the window sections, usually insufficient for anyone to get through. However, if the lower window section is left raised by the 3" it could well be enough to remove ornaments, jewellery etc., left in too close proximity, so a loss (maybe quite substantial) could occur without the burglar actually having to enter the building.

The fact that the window cannot easily be opened further than the said 3" often gives the building's occupant a false sense of security, to the extent of leaving the window open when the premises are unoccupied, an open invitation to vandals and arsonists, the present scourge of our society.

Casement Windows

(i) Casement fastener — see figure 55. This is a simple and very obvious handle, and should be used as such and not as a security device. It is affixed to the opening section and is a simple pivoted piece of metal which engages over the fixed adjoining frame.

(ii) Casement stay — see figure 56. Yet another very simple device, being a hinged metal bar with several holes in it, the bar being attached to the opening section of the window. The fixed adjoining frame has two metal spikes engaged in the holes when the window is closed, whereas when open only one spike is in a hole. Apart from the obvious security defects, if the window is left open and a wind gets up the window vibration can cause the bar to *'jump'* allowing the window to swing free and be damaged.

An older version of the above, but still found quite frequently, is that illustrated in figure 57. The metal bar is hinge fixed to the opening section of the window and then passes through a hinged rectangular *'tube'* fixed to the adjoining frame. Passing through this *'tube'* is a finger operated screw which can be tightened to stop the bar slipping through, thus providing adjustable amounts of opening as do the spikes in the previous example.

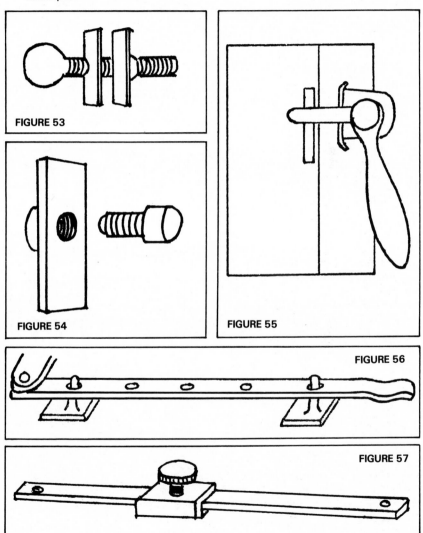

FIGURE 53

FIGURE 54

FIGURE 55

FIGURE 56

FIGURE 57

Sliding Windows

These often come with no devices other than a handle. If you are lucky, they may have a small, weak claw lock operated by a singer slide, and therefore, not in my opinion a lock at all. Similar devices are found on sliding patio doors.

Fanlights

(i) Top hinged fanlights are usually fitted with casement stays as illustrated in figure 56, and operating on exactly the same principle.

(ii) Bottom hinged fanlights are fitted with a catch as shown in figure 58, the bolt being bevelled and operating in a similar way to that in a cylinder rimlatch. To retract the bolt, a hook is passed through the eye which is then pulled down. There is a staple screwed to the fixed adjoining frame.

To prevent breakage and restrict the opening area there must be restraints otherwise the fanlight would fall down through 180°. These restraints are known as quadrant stays (or cradle bars), and are shown in figure 59, being comparatively thin pieces of shaped metal with a *'lug'* on the end and are attached to the adjoining framework. Unfortunately, these stays (sometimes there is only one) are easy to bend sideways, thus allowing the fanlight to drop and entry to be made. To over-come this, I prefer to see a quadrant bar as shown in figure 60 where the two stays are joined together. One must ensure that the permitted opening allowed by the quadrant bar is not sufficient to allow a person to enter. The bar should be affixed to the frame-work by non-return screws.

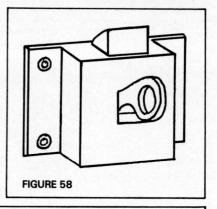

FIGURE 58

(iii) The louvred type have virtually no securing devices, purely a handle for opening and closing.

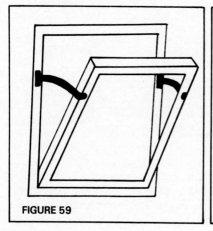

FIGURE 59

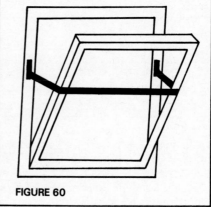

FIGURE 60

CHAPTER 9
Windows — Locks & Physical Protection

I would remind you of the distinction I made, in the Chapter on Door Locks, between securing devices which are finger operated and locks which are key operated. However, there is a comparatively recent development where locks are *'engaged'* by finger pressure only but to release the lock a key must be used. These are, in my opinion, locks.

WINDOW LOCKS
Window locks are used for the same reason as door locks, viz. securing an opening section to a fixed section, or two opening sections to each other so that within a fixed frame neither can move. However, because of the window lock's comparatively small size related to door locks, it is not possible to have high security — because the key operation is simple the keys themselves are simple, not numerous in type or differs, so it is not difficult to obtain sufficient keys to open most window locks.

Due to these restrictions there is little point in going into great detail, but various examples are illustrated in figures 61-67 overleaf.

Basically these locks set about their task in one of three ways. Firstly, there can be a moving (or removable) section which, when withdrawn, allows complete freedom of movement of the window, but when in the locked position it secures the opening and fixed sections together. Secondly, you can have the same principle but with an intermediate stage where the window is locked partially open, but cannot, without the use of the key, be opened further or closed completely. The third method is whereby a standard *'handle'* for the window can be immobilised when the window is closed. Those illustrated form only a small sample on the market, and the reader must examine any he meets, see if the principle involved is appropriate for the window to which it is fixed, and that it is properly affixed and operational. It is not uncommon to find good locks fitted, but the wrong lock for the window involved, an example of DIY and *'cowboy'* jobs. Fitting window locks is not always as easy as it sounds, especially if the frames are narrow, as the drilling of holes can cause glass breakage. A note of caution when prescribing specific locks; manufacturers' brochures appear to deal only with window frames where all edges have nice 90° angles. Unfortunately, all the window manufacturers have nasty habits of producing windows with fancy edges and varying angles, so although some locks might appear appropriate they will not operate unless part of the lock is *'padded out'* or parts of the frame *'cut away'* to achieve the correct angle, neither producing an acceptable answer from an appearance point of view, and probably a less than required efficiency from a security aspect. Not that you are likely to meet this but I was told by a surveyor that he had encountered the ultimate in stupidity, viz. a manufacturer's brochure had a photograph of a particular lock fitted. So that the method of fitting could be seen clearly, the window frame in the photograph had the adjoining piece of wood removed. Regrettably, the DIY client had done exactly as shown on the photograph and had a chunk of frame missing. Now you know why surveyors must be prepared to meet anything — and keep a straight face!

One type of window mentioned in the previous Chapter which is not catered for by any of the locks illustrated is the louvre, simply because I know of no lock designed to protect it which is effective.

When carrying out a survey you should try to ascertain where the keys are kept; hopefully not in the lock. That is all too often exactly what does happen, but the client will always have some sort of explanation for this *'temporary'* failure.

Before leaving window locks let me remind you of what may to some appear obvious, i.e. locks do not mean an entry cannot be made. All you are doing is stopping the frame from being opened easily, not stopping the glass being broken.

PHYSICAL PROTECTION
1. **Bricking up** — This may seem rather obvious but it is still worthy of some notes. If a window is not required at all, why keep it?; it is only a temptation to Burglar Bill. However, if you are going to have a window bricked, do it properly. It is all too common to find completely botched

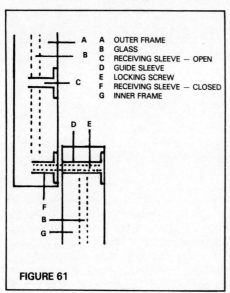

A A OUTER FRAME
B B GLASS
   C RECEIVING SLEEVE — OPEN
   D GUIDE SLEEVE
C E LOCKING SCREW
   F RECEIVING SLEEVE — CLOSED
   G INNER FRAME

FIGURE 61

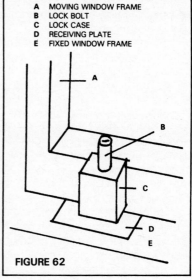

A MOVING WINDOW FRAME
B LOCK BOLT
C LOCK CASE
D RECEIVING PLATE
E FIXED WINDOW FRAME

FIGURE 62

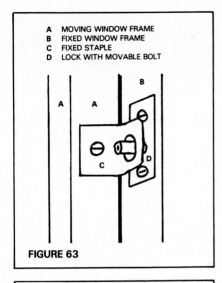

A   MOVING WINDOW FRAME
B   FIXED WINDOW FRAME
C   FIXED STAPLE
D   LOCK WITH MOVABLE BOLT

FIGURE 63

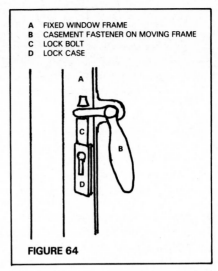

A   FIXED WINDOW FRAME
B   CASEMENT FASTENER ON MOVING FRAME
C   LOCK BOLT
D   LOCK CASE

FIGURE 64

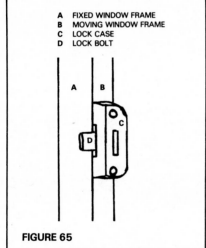

A   FIXED WINDOW FRAME
B   MOVING WINDOW FRAME
C   LOCK CASE
D   LOCK BOLT

FIGURE 65

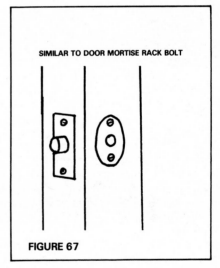

SIMILAR TO DOOR MORTISE RACK BOLT

FIGURE 67

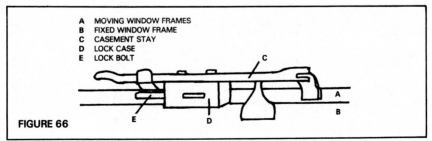

A   MOVING WINDOW FRAMES
B   FIXED WINDOW FRAME
C   CASEMENT STAY
D   LOCK CASE
E   LOCK BOLT

FIGURE 66

59

jobs with all sorts of building materials, not only presenting an eyesore but patently obvious weaknesses, especially if you are not precise about your requirements. The most common fault is to find the *'hole'* plugged with bricks the exact shape of the hole. The bricks should be *'bonded'* to the surrounding bricks, i.e. no half-bricks etc. used to fill holes. Apart from being more presentable this produces a result with greater strength, the area of new brickwork being 'bonded' into the original adjoining bricks. Any timber sills or lintels must be removed. The infill should be the same thickness as the adjoining wall, whereas you will often find *'indentation'* internally when the wall is flush externally. These indentations may be seen by deliverymen, meter readers, tradesmen etc. who may, if so inclined, spread the word. If you are dealing with an old building try and get used (secondhand) bricks otherwise the difference in colour will stand out, externally at least.

2. **Metal lining or facing** — It is usually not possible to do this very satisfactorily, because although there might (only might) be sufficient timber in the framework adjoining the brickwork, there will almost certainly not be enough in the middle of the window so there will be insufficient fixing points for coach bolts or screws, and unless the job can be done properly it should not be attempted. There must be fixing points all around the edge, down and across the middle (or very close thereto). As with doors, the maximum distance between coach bolts should be 6" and if non-return screws are used they should be at 4" intervals with countersunk heads. If the middle fixing points are not present this could be overcome by having metal straps welded across the sheeting and bolted to the frame, or if the opening is to be lined and faced, timber battens can be inserted and fixed to provide central fixing points for the metal.

   I do not like to see lining done on its own, my reasoning being that this would result in the glass not being seen by the client (unless the area is regularly inspected externally — not likely if to the rear of the building) and if it becomes broken and develops the uncared for appearance, it becomes an invitation for attack.

   The metal used should be the same as for door facing etc, previously mentioned.

3. **Timber lining** — In the main the same comments apply except that almost certainly the timber would have to be internal to protect against weathering. Plywood or chipboard at least $\frac{3}{8}$" should be used. Because of the weather problem and the probability of broken (external) glass, this is not a form of security I like to see; *'boarded up windows,'* which is virtually what we are talking about, always give the building a run down appearance in my opinion.

4. **Metal Bars** — Although the materials, dimensions etc were mentioned earlier under door protection I feel that as you are more likely to encounter bars with windows that it is worthy of repetition here. The bars

must be solid round iron not less than $\frac{5}{8}$ths of an inch in diameter, OR solid square iron not less than $\frac{5}{8}$ths of an inch in section, OR solid flat iron not less than 1" in breadth and $\frac{3}{8}$ths of an inch in thickness. The distance between the centres of adjoining bars, or between an end bar and the adjoining masonry or frame, must not exceed 4" (years ago this used to be 5", but this proved to be too great — from experience of losses). Where bars are greater in length than 4'11", tie bars must be fitted at 2'6" intervals. A tie bar is a flat metal bar 1" in breadth and $\frac{3}{8}$ths of an inch in thickness (as mentioned above) through which holes are drilled at the same spacing as the vertical bars. These bars obviously fit through the holes, the principle being that the tie bars prevent the vertical bars from being spread sideways, something which is not too difficult with long bars if the tie bars are not present.

These bars can be fitted as follows:-

(a) As in figure 68 where each bar is sunk individually into the brickwork. Tie bars have to be sunk into the masonry also, and welded to the bars at each intersection. Unfortunately, some people fit these bars by hacking out pieces of brick, inserting the bars and recementing. Whilst this may be acceptable for the tie bars, it is not for the other bars because all you end up with is weak bricks which can be easily withdrawn. The more correct method is to drill holes in the brickwork and drop the bars in, securing with mortar.

(b) As in figure 69 where the bars are all welded to a framework of flat iron not less than 1" in breadth and $\frac{3}{8}$" thick. Tie bars are also welded to this framework. All of this is carried out in the manufacturer's premises and arrives ready to be installed. The frame is then secured to the masonry by bolts sunk into predrilled holes and, once installed, the bolt heads should be welded to prevent removal. It will be seen that the removal of one or even two bolts will not allow the removal of the whole frame. This is the method which, personally, I prefer.

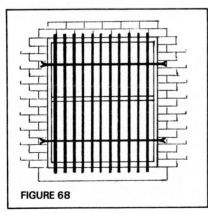

FIGURE 68

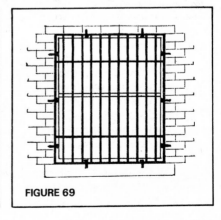

FIGURE 69

5. **Rigid metal grilles** — There are many ways in which these are similar to those mentioned under glass door protection, but as there are also many differences I feel the topic is worthy of full mention here.

   The manner in which the grilles are constructed is the same as for doors. Rigid metal grilles are seldom fitted internally to windows, especially in shops, as displays, furniture etc. prevent easy access thereto if they are to be removed daily, or even occasionally, for window cleaning. If you can have the grilles fitted internally so much the better as they are less likely to be attacked, but in most cases you will be very lucky to achieve this.

   Assuming, therefore, that they are on the outside it follows that the fixings etc. are all important. The grille frame must obstruct all screwheads (unless the non return — countersunk-type are used), otherwise the whole lot can be taken down quite easily and, who knows, they might be stolen as well as anything else taken. This might sound a bit daft, but I can think of three reasons for taking the grilles, (i) they might be useful somewhere else, (ii) to leave them lying around would only draw attention to the burglary, and (iii) before they are replaced there could be a period without grilles present, and a subsequent break-in would be easier. Once again, good quality padlocks are a must otherwise the considerable expense involved will have been wasted. There are many frames, where two windows meet, which are so thin that it is difficult to fit any hardware. Where this is the case it is quite common for a metal rod (detachable) to be fitted vertically from the ground to a fitting in the facia or transom, and the grilles fitted to these rods which have integral brackets. In some instances these rods will be too thin and long and liable to be bent out of their housings, something to watch for. Another situation where these rods may be used is in shop fronts with recessed doorways, and the grilles go across the entire shopfront on the building line instead of going all round the *'lobby'* which would be much more expensive.

6. **Folding metal grilles** — sometimes called collapsible grilles. These are found mainly on the inside of shop display windows. The grilles are roughly the same design as the *'open brick'* metal roller shutter but the materials are usually not quite as strong. To the bottom plate there are sometimes slip bolt type locks to fit into adjoining brackets, and if need be these can be padlocked or *'contacted'* into an alarm system to ensure the grille is *'down'* when the premises are closed. They can be raised out of sight above the window by means of a handle, ratchet and pulleys, not into a roll (as with metal roller shutters) but into a condensed block as all the sections are hinged. There is a definite need for this type of protection but readers are warned not to ask for it without careful consideration as it is costly both to install and to maintain.

7. **Bostwick Gates** are folding grilles but differ from those above in two major ways, (1) they fold sideways as opposed to running up and down, and (2) the metal used is usually much stronger. They resemble the old

fashioned type of lift or hoist gate. You will encounter them in both single and double leaf form and nearly always they incorporate a form of mortise claw lock; failing that, they are substantial enough for a good chain and padlock. They should, wherever possible, be fitted internally as they are too expensive to leave exposed to vandalism etc.

8.   **Metal Roller Shutters** — These have been described earlier under doors and figures 6 and 7, and this should be re-read in this connection as the same comments apply, except that obviously there will be no *'wicket gate'* when they are protecting windows.

CHAPTER 10

Alarm protection of Doors and Windows

In previous chapters dealing with doors and windows we have mentioned means of protection, but purely from a physical aspect.

Although we have not yet dealt with Burglar Alarms (that is the more commonly used descriptive term although it is more properly termed an Intruder Alarm because not all intruders are burglars) in any detail, I feel that we must, at this stage, deal with door and window protection by this method before leaving these openings altogether. Later in the book alarms will be dealt with further. One point which must be made right now, however, is that alarms are not designed to stop people making an entry into an alarmed premises, they are designed to indicate that this has happened. It is then up to someone to take the appropriate action.

A **Alarm Contacts** are devices which are intended to indicate that a door or openable window has been opened when it should not have been. This very intention has a secondary, but important, use in that it can be a means of indicating that a window or door which has been in use has not been closed (e.g. windows opened in hot weather, also Fire Exit doors which are often opened for ventilation) and the alarm should not be able to be set when closing the premises until this situation has been rectified.

As door contacts were one of the first pieces of alarm equipment to be developed you will, unfortunately, come across some of the older types still in use. Currently, in the majority of cases, the contact works on the principle that a magnet brings together two pieces of metal through which an electric current passes. Remove the magnet and the two pieces of metal separate, the circuit is broken and an alarm condition is caused. Some old systems worked on virtually an opposite principle i.e. a projection was forced between two pieces of metal to complete the circuit; remove the projection and the circuit was broken with the same results. This type of contact is prone to malfunction due to dirt on the projection causing incomplete contacts, and also *'sticking parts'* meaning the circuit is still complete when it shouldn't be.

Usually the two pieces of metal forming the circuit are housed in the door frame and the magnet in the door itself. When flush mounted (i.e. set into the door frame and door) they are virtually invisible to the casual viewer when the door is closed, especially as nowadays the components are getting smaller and smaller. Surface mounted contacts are not sunk into the door and are especially suitable for metal doors. It is obviously quicker to surface mount the contact rather than sink it into the door and, unfortunately, some installers surface mount when there is no need, presumably for speed and a quick job. I deplore this practice as it is obvious that, where practicable, hidden security is best. For large doors, metal roller shutters and the like, where the contacts are subject to heavier wear and tear, there are special heavy duty contacts specifically designed to stand up to these rigours. The fact that they are big and heavy should not make them any less sensitive or efficient.

Opening windows are usually much smaller than doors, so there should be no need to use the heavy duty type of contact. You can have each opening section involved contacted (preferably flush mounted, but if not, e.g. metal frames, then surface mounted) into the alarm system. You are unlikely to come across *'old contacts'* in existing systems as window contacting is a comparatively recent trend.

B. **Alarm Wiring** — Fine, hard drawn, plastic covered, copper wire is attached to the door surface by means of metal staples which, to avoid the chance of false alarms, should be insulated. The wiring should be at a specific spacing as laid down by British Standard 4737: Specification for Intruder Alarm Systems in Buildings, and *'taken off'* the door with much heavier coated wire at the hinge side. This *'take off'* wire should be sufficiently long to allow the door to open fully without pulling at the wire junctions. At the same time, this wire should not be too long otherwise it might be trapped in the door when it is closed, thus causing the wires to break. The wire used on the door should be sufficiently tight (kept in place by the staples) so that it cannot be moved more than a minimal amount without breaking, thus causing an alarm to be indicated. Because the wire is fairly fragile it can easily be damaged and must be protected, usually by a sheet of hardboard being nailed over the entire doorface. In the vast majority of cases the surveyor sees the fitting after it is finished and the actual wiring cannot be seen. You end up with little option but to accept, and hope, that the job has been done properly.

As the wire is attached to the door by staples, it is obvious that only all timber doors are suitable for this type of protection.

To obtain a flat surface some doors have to have mouldings and beadings removed, but care must be exercised in case the beading removal loosens the door panels.

Ledged and braced doors present a problem because of the uneven surface, the method of overcoming this being to wire the door in triangles between the ledges and braces. However, the hardboard protection is not all that strong, so battens may have to be attached to the door and the hardboard nailed to the battens, ledges and braces. No battens are usually required with ledged, braced and framed doors.

In old, pre BS 4737, installations only one wire was used so it was not too difficult to *'loop out'* the system, but the more modern system uses two or more wires to make this more difficult, but not impossible.

Where very high security is required then the wiring can be *'laced'* i.e. fitted to the door vertically and horizontally, to give double protection.

This method of protection can also be used where windows have been internally boarded, but care should be taken to ensure that the wiring is led on at one corner and taken off diagonally opposite, otherwise it could be possible to move *'the wired panel'* from the wall so long as the corner with the take-off wiring was held fast. Another means of achieving the same thing is to have loops taken off at each corner and the loops attached to the adjoining masonry etc.

C **Tube and Wiring** is another means of protecting doors, door glass and windows, and in the opinion of many is by far the most reliable method available. Unfortunately, there is little argument that it is not a method of protection which could be considered as pleasing on the eye, therefore care and common sense must be used when prescribing this form of protection.

In essence the protection is the same as (B) above, but this method is used where it is not possible to staple the alarm wiring directly onto the surface to be protected — because the surface in question will simply not take staples, nothing to do with appearance etc.

What you have is comparatively thin aluminium tubing in a timber frame (top and bottom), the ends of the tubes actually fitting into holes in the timber. The timber is secured, by screws, on to the surface to be protected, or on to its immediate surround. Alarm wiring, of exactly the same type as is used in (B) above, is fed through these aluminium tubes and passed from one tube to another via channels cut into the timber. These channels must be concealed by fillets of timber so that the wiring is not exposed and liable to damage or manipulation. In order that the entire alarmed tube and wired frame is not removed from its location, the frame should be attached to the protected surface by means of "live" alarm wiring loops, preferably at all four corners of the frame (but usually only a maximum of two will ever be found).

Once again there are specific requirements for this type of protection, the detail being contained in BS 4737.

It is still quite common to encounter tubed and wired protection installed prior to the publication of BS4737 and, due to the lack of any standard or reference at the time of installation, the form of protection can vary quite considerably. Examples of some of the poor features of these older systems are: (a) *'Single wire systems'* i.e. only one wire which goes through all tubes thus making *'looping out'* comparatively easy, (b) the metal tube containing the wire has a seam or join running its full length, making it possible to *'prise open'* the tube and expose the wire within, (c) no timber frame, the tubes being held onto the protected surface by metal saddles and the wire literally coming out of the top of one tube, running exposed across the door surface, and into the next tube, (d) timber framed, but the wiring just running across the timber surface and in no way hidden. None of these practices are now permissible if the alarm system is said to be to BS 4737, so if you do encounter them it is either an old or *'rogue'* system.

Regarding windows, tube and wiring is virtually the only form of protection suitable for louvres or leaded glass. However, with windows there can sometimes be installation problems because some windows (unlike most doors) have peculiar shapes. Care must also be exercised with inward opening windows which are to remain in use.

Where the risk is higher than average it is possible for vibration detectors to be fitted to the tubed and wired frame to detect anyone trying to interfere with the wiring or frame.

D. **Knock-out Rods** — This is an old form of glass protection, which is a variation of the tubed and wired frames mentioned in (C) above. The rods of metal did **not** contain any wiring, but were held in place by springs in a timber frame which was screwed onto the door. The electric current was in wires onto the top frame, and conducted through *'contacts'* at the end of each rod, hence the removal of a rod broke the circuit causing an alarm. An improved version of this protection had current running through both the top and bottom frame making rod removal without causing an alarm *very* difficult. Whilst an updated version of this type of protection is permissible under BS 4737 (in that the standard does not cater for it or control it), it is seldom used, so you can assume that any you meet form part of an old system; and not to be recommended.

E. **Metal Foil Tape** — This is a thin, fairly narrow, metallic tape which is fixed to glass by means of an adhesive, then a coating of clear varnish is applied for protection. There is virtually no physical strength in the tape, it being there purely to conduct electric current and thus complete an alarm circuit. The end of the tape is fed into a small plastic *'junction box'* which itself is glued onto the glass, and the alarm wiring is also fed into the junction box thus completing the circuit. If the glass is in more than one panel then the connection between each sheet of glass should be by means of junction boxes and alarm wiring and not by simply continuing the foil from one pane of glass to the other, in some cases over a timber frame. Unfortunately, this cost cutting (cheating) method is used and must be rectified whenever encountered.

Foil tape can only satisfactorily be applied to perfectly flat glass, consequently it cannot (or should not) be used on the uneven surfaces of reeded, pebbled or other similar types of glass with even a very slightly rough surface. Most of these glasses have a rough and a smooth surface, so make sure which side you are dealing with before asking for foil tape. The tape, of course, is fitted to the inside surface.

All of the specifications for the type, measurements and design of the tape and its application are controlled by BS 4737.

The principle in this form of protection is that if the glass is broken, the foil breaks also, breaking the circuit and causing an alarm condition.

If this form of protection is used on windows with opening sections (not often encountered) it must be used with extreme care because of the possibility of the wiring becoming caught in between two pieces of timber and damaged. Beware clients who say *'oh that window is never opened anyway',* as a change of staff may also change habits.

F. **Vibration Type Detectors** — I have intentionally used the word *'type'* as there are a great number of variations on the same theme, the detectors relying on vibration or sound transference through the protected surface to activate the equipment. The theory is that anyone trying to smash, cut etc., their way through the door or window will cause either noise or vibration. Unfortunately, so do many other things which are innocent and legal, the result being false alarms. The better models of this type of equipment have analysers which can eliminate (in theory) unwanted signals, and they are better than non analysed types. The degree of sensitivity can be adjusted to cater for the materials involved and the general location, which appears to be a good point but can also mean it can be adjusted for the wrong reasons. How do you gauge accurately whether or not the correct sensitivity setting has been chosen? By breaking the surface involved? Not very practical.

The detection unit itself is quite small (in the region of 1½" square) and is attached directly to the surface to be protected, by adhesive. If the general atmosphere is hot, or the glass is directly in the sun's rays, the adhesive will *'dry out'* and the unit may well hang off the relevant surface; almost a certain recipe for false alarms.

Even if installed and maintained properly, and used in conjunction with proper analysers, I am not convinced of the suitability of these units. It certainly seems improper to use them on doors subject to mischief by children, drunks etc., vibration from road traffic, and the like. If used on internal doors be careful in case the alarm is *'partially set'* when work continues on one side of the door (for late work and the like) prior to full setting of the alarm.

Unfortunately, in my opinion, these units are easily installed and liable to be used to cut costs where competition is involved. Not a happy prospect.

There is a tendency to have these pieces of equipment on dwelling house windows and, in many cases, that might be all right, but care must be taken relative to bushes etc. which may hit against the windows on stormy nights.

On no account should they be used on doors or windows which are not in good condition and tight fitting.

G. **Break Glass Detectors** — These are smallish devices which are **not** fixed to the glass but to a part of the building, in very close proximity to the glass involved. They are designed to pick up the sound of broken glass, but also, on many occasions, react to sources of ultra sound, radio frequencies, vehicle brakes and other legitimate noises. There is an element of noise screening in the unit but this is not always reliable. They are useful pieces of equipment, but only if extra special care is taken in considering all location factors, which incidentally might change dramatically some time after installation, and some of which might not be apparent at the time of the survey.

CHAPTER 11

Building Openings other than Doors and Windows

In previous chapters we have considered doors and windows and their protection on the basis that they were the most numerous legal openings, regrettably often used for illegal purposes. In this chapter we will consider a variety of openings, less numerous in each building, but overall sufficiently significant to warrant attention. No undue significance should be placed on the order in which they are mentioned.

Trap Doors — These are horizontal doors found in several different situations, the most common of which are: (a) From a pavement into a cellar, usually used for access of bulky goods without them having to go through the main premises. Probably the most common example is in public houses. (b) From a loft into the topmost floor, often used for access to water tanks etc. (c) Between floors of a multi-storey building for access of heavy goods by means of pulleys. Sometimes these trap doors are shaped, or have holes therein for the passage of ropes etc.

These internal trap doors are often found in old or large buildings which were formerly in one occupancy but which are now multi-tenanted. To make matters worse they may be disused and obscured by false ceilings and the like; this makes an inspection of adjoining floors even more desirable but this is often not possible.

Protection obviously depends upon the degree of risk involved, but as a minimum they should be secured on your client's side. Probably the most acceptable way of achieving this is by use of padlocking bolts, but remember the hinge pin may be on the *'other side'* of the door, so hinge bolts may be necessary. Where appropriate, the door should be contacted into an intruder alarm system and may be wired in addition. In other words treat the trap door in the same way as a door met in a vertical situation and protect accordingly.

Points of caution to be remembered are: (1) In some cases these trap doors are fire exits so permanent or lockable security may not be permissible. (2) If the trap door is in an *'external'* situation e.g. a pavement or onto a flat roof, it is inevitable that weathering will be significant and special alarm equipment of a water resistant nature must be used; standard alarm wiring may not be possible. Locking bolts etc. must also suffer eventually and may have to be replaced.

Hoist Doors and **lift doors** should be treated alike.One principal problem arises in multi-tenure buildings where these hoist openings are not into a communal part of the building but directly into the client's own portion. This will probably mean that access can be obtained from another tenant's part of the building and your client will have no control over their security. Even if the hoist is immobilised *'out of hours'* this still leaves the hoist shaft as a means of getting from floor to floor. Once again, if your risk warrants it, then the hoist doors to your client's premises must be secured, and depending upon the door construction and method of opening, that may not be easy. Remember, most of these doors slide, overlap and even (when open) disappear into framework, and nothing must be affixed to the door to prevent this. Because there is such a variety of circumstances I am not going to suggest anything in case it is misinterpreted, but urge you to closely examine each case as it arises. If the premises are alarmed then a contact on the door is not difficult to install, but remember hoist vibrations caused by someone (working later than your client) using the hoist might cause false alarms if this is not considered at the time of installation.

Pavement Lights — These are blocks of glass, usually square (about 4" x 4") and approx. 2" thick, set into either a metal or concrete frame. Like trap doors, they are usually found in a horizontal plane, used for giving light into a basement or cellar. However, you will also find them in flat roofs giving light to the floor below. If you encounter a metal frame it is reasonable to assume they are fairly old, concrete being the modern way of fixing. Although glass, these blocks are not easy to break, and even if one is broken the hole does not present a major opening from a burglary aspect, although it may well be serious from a fire or special perils aspect. If you consider the risk heavy, then protection may be necessary but be careful of using electrical devices, once again because of water related problems if breakage of glass does occur. Internal bars may be more suitable, if necessary backed up by *'electronic space protection'* which will be mentioned later.

In recent years there has been a development of having this type of glass assembly in vertical walls, presumably where strength and light are both required. The same comments as above apply, except that electronic alarming should be possible (tube and wiring) as water should not present a problem.

Pavement Bars — In older buildings, you will find, in basements, vertical windows leading into an area beneath pavement level. At pavement level, protecting this *'area'* or *'hole'* are metal bars secured to the pavement and the building; a horizontal grille designed as weight bearing. Because they are usually associated with older buildings it follows that in many cases the bars must be old and consequently weakened; and it may be that the window itself will require additional protection.

The main problems with these bars actually arise in connection with liability insurance (people tripping on poorly maintained bars) and fire insurance (waste and lighted materials being dropped between the bars), and composite surveyors should note.

Stallrisers — See figure 70. This is the area beneath the glass of a shop window, and obviously varies in size depending on the shop front design. This can be of a variety of materials varying between brick, concrete block, metal, glass and timber, or a combination thereof, and also of varying thickness. If there is a shelf or display in the window, finding the detail can be

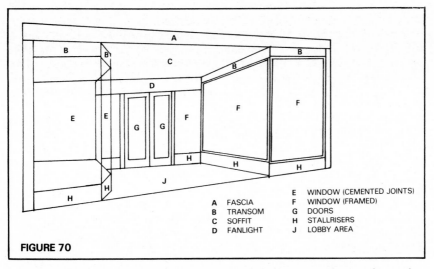

		E	WINDOW (CEMENTED JOINTS)
A	FASCIA	F	WINDOW (FRAMED)
B	TRANSOM	G	DOORS
C	SOFFIT	H	STALLRISERS
D	FANLIGHT	J	LOBBY AREA

FIGURE 70

very difficult, but you can bet Burglar Bill will find any weakness. Assuming you can assess the problem, if any, and if you decide protection is necessary, the methods available are as for any other building part constructed of similar material. However, bear one important point in your mind. If you had difficulty getting access to the area so would tradesmen who you want to install the protection. This could result in increased costs and, equally importantly, increase the likelihood of lack of maintenance of the protective device.

You will encounter instances where the ground floor is actually slightly above the pavement level. The stallrisers of these *"ground floor"* windows can, in fact, be windows from a basement.

Transoms, Soffits and Fascias — These are, once again, associated primarily with shop fronts and apt to be forgotten because they are often disguised. Once again, refer to figure 70 where these are shown. They are all parts of the shop front which are above eye level in a situation where the display etc. tends to distract the eye. The transom and fascia are often either decorated or obscured by lettering and the like. In the illustration, the soffit is beneath the fascia level and, therefore, probably constructed of lightweight material i.e., virtually a false ceiling, whereas in other cases the fascia may be against the building itself, and consequently the soffit is the ceiling itself. What you are in effect looking for is lightweight materials (often plastic) which lead into a void or false ceiling area giving access to the shop itself. If the risk is sufficiently hazardous e.g. a furrier or jeweller particularly, but often with less hazardous risks, then these areas must be considered from a protection aspect just as much as the doors and windows.

It is quite often the case that having entered the shop itself, if you turn around and look above the door, you will find a lightweight wall being a backing to the aforementioned void, and it is probably easiest to protect the lightweight wall. However, you must remember this does not protect against entry to the display window via the void.

Showcases — An *'island showcase'* is usually located in the lobby area of a shopfront which has a recessed doorway and, although some of these do remain, I feel they are dying out. The island showcase is an independent showcase which does not communicate with the rest of the shop, and it has its own doorway. It is usually glass with a lightweight, fairly low, ceiling although some do go up to the level of the soffit. Because it is a fairly filmsy structure it is usually not possible to fit a decent lock to the door, and unless the showcase ceiling does go up to the soffit it is not possible to lay wiring to alarm the showcase (that is unless the client is prepared to let you dig up his lobby floor, which is extremely unlikely). Unless the entire shopfront is protected by grilles or a metal roller shutter which encloses the lobby, then I feel this type of showcase is virtually a case of *'accept it as it stands'* or *'limit the attraction therein'*, as you can't do anything to additionally protect it.

Wall mounted showcases occur where the entire frontage is recessed leaving wall space between the display window and the pavement line. On the side wall you may find a similarly weak display cabinet which is equally difficult to protect except that you may be able to run (protected) alarm wire along the wall to alarm the showcase. However, this type of showcase is usually quite small and the value of the contents may not justify the expense.

I would suggest that if the contents do cause you concern then you should endeavour to get the client to move them. These showcases are so small that *"smash and grab"* is childs play (often literally) and no alarm will prevent that.

Rooflights — These come in a tremendous variety of shapes and sizes and are an ever increasing *'opening'* you will encounter. Having said that, unless they are well maintained they are a constant source of water damage problems as they tend to leak. Because of this they are often covered over by roofing felt or some similar material and therefore less easy to detect unless the outer surface of the roof can be inspected. They can also be easily obscured by false ceilings and the like, so you see they can be a great source of trouble for more than one reason.

These rooflights can be metal or timber framed, flush with the roof or raised therefrom, fixed or opening (manually or by ratchet mechanism), with or without ventilation slats (which themselves may be fixed or moveable), ordinary or wired glass, plastic, fibreglass etc. etc. So you see you are liable to meet a vast array, but from a theft aspect I doubt if it really matters. The location is probably more important, viz, easily seen from other buildings, liable to malicious damage by children etc. The openings themselves are virtually all weak so they are either vulnerable or not, and consequently must be protected or not.

If you wish to protect against malicious children etc. (breakage causing water damage to anything beneath) then the protection must be external. It is possible to have metal mesh shaped and attached to a frame which should be secured to the roof by means of rawbolts or the like, but this must be done professionally or the bolts themselves will cause water leakage. Depending on the rooflight shape and frame, it may be possible to attach the grille frame thereto, but if this is done we return to our coach bolts or non-return screws.

However, none of the protection in the previous paragraph can really be considered protection against true burglars. This may appear strange as this form of protection was mentioned in connection with windows. However, the windows are more likely to be seen than rooflights, as is anyone trying to attack them.

I feel it is best to protect these features against burglars by internal equipment, be it physical or electronic, but how this is achieved depends on the rooflight design and, if the rooflight is the opening type, if this opening facility is used?

From a purely physical aspect, probably the best method of protection is metal bars using the same specification as for windows,mentioned in a previous chapter. However, if the goods being protected are thin, the obvious example being clothing, then they can be *'fished'* through the bars. To get around this problem, metal mesh can be added to the bars or additional bars added at right angles to the first set. Metal mesh on its own may not be strong enough unless extremely good quality is used and it is exceptionally well secured.

Using intruder alarm equipment may be efficient but you must bear in mind the water seepage aspect, i.e. unless the rooflights are kept in good condition, water could cause false alarms by getting into the alarm equipment. Probably the most popular use of alarm equipment in this connection is tubed and wired frames, but the *fishing'* problem mentioned previously applies here also, so two frames at right angles may be necessary. Vibration detection is another method used, but care must be exercised if the roof is a haunt of cats which could cause false alarms.

I urge caution and use of commonsense when protecting rooflights. It is not really sensible to have costly equipment on a rooflight set in an otherwise fragile roof (e.g. corrugated asbestos), unless the whole roof is being protected. You may consider this an obvious point to make but I assure you I have seen it done, and the burglar leaves the rooflight and comes in through the roof itself!

CHAPTER 12
Walls and Roofs

Up to this stage of the book we have concentrated on describing and protecting openings in buildings which are there by design. Now we have to consider the making of openings by the Burglar. A great number of losses arise out of the burglar fraternity using brute force against the building structure and literally coming through walls and roofs. Obviously, this is easier where these materials are not of the strongest nature in the first place.

Not so many years ago the majority of buildings were constructed of traditional materials, i.e. brick, stone, timber and the like, and roofed with slates, tiles or timber. Whilst these materials are obviously still used, there is today an increase in the use of *'modern'* materials, e.g. plastics and metal, which can be erected more speedily as they are in large sheets. This speed of building obviously reduces the time factor and tradesmen's time costs money. Ally this to the fact that the material itself is cheaper than the more traditional materials and you can see the cost advantages of this type of building. With some modern offices the major part of many external walls is glass and, depending on the quality used, this is not particularly burglar resistant. Unfortunately, from a security viewpoint, the extensive use of glass is creeping into many buildings of varying uses.

The main effect from a security aspect is an increase in comparatively lightweight, and consequently burglary prone, buildings, presenting increased problems. You will, of course, still see the other types of construction as numerically those buildings still vastly outnumber the newer structures, the exception to that state of affairs possibly being in *'new towns'*, *'development areas'* and *'industrial estates'*. You are, therefore, going to be faced with a considerable array of different constructions, possibly even within a single risk, due to extensions. I also have little doubt that scientific developments will produce even more materials in the future and their problems, as yet unknown, will have to be faced as they arise.

If you look at the older stone and brick buildings they give an impression of solidity and strength which, in the majority of cases, is a true one. However, initial impressions can sometimes be misleading. Lack of maintenance, misuse, abnormal occupancy (e.g. constant wet processes) can result in crumbling and loose materials, which may be easy to remove without much noise or necessity for expert knowledge. I know of at least one part of Britain where it is well known that the area below sinks is usually weak in older buildings. (Letters signed by all four grandparents of the writer, and accompanied by a donation to my favourite charity, might prise this classified information from me).

Modern *'concrete block'* buildings can be either strong or weak depending, amongst other things, on the type of block used — some are much harder than others. Building regulations are concerned primarily with load bearing ability and resistance to heat, but resistance to hammer and chisel is not necessarily achieved with the same constituent materials. Some of these blocks are *'hollow'* but you will not be able to tell that from looking at them in a wall.

With all these *'solid'* structures one of the most important factors is the building mortar; was it properly mixed, properly applied etc? The chances are that just by looking you will not be able to tell.

The object of the three preceding paragraphs is not to spread panic or dismay but simply to warn you against being fooled by initial impressions and preconceived ideas. Regardless of the construction materials used, the general condition and standard of maintenance is always important and could, in extreme cases, mean a *'lightweight'* building is better than a *'solid weight'* building from a security aspect. This is also a very good reason for having regular re-surveys to check on maintenance standards.

Despite what has just been said it is true that, generally speaking, concrete (even better if reinforced), brick and stone buildings are strongest, metal being next on the list, with timber and asbestos being weakest. Unfortunately, many metal and asbestos buildings are bolted together with the nuts on the outside, so a spanner can be used to virtually dismantle the wall concerned. Strangely enough, this doesn't happen all that often, probably because it is easier to bash a hole and gain entry that way, noisier but quicker.

In multi-tenure buildings internal walls may well, as far as your client is concerned, be his perimeter and obviously of extreme importance. In older, traditionally built structures, internal walls are very often thinner than external walls, whereas in many modern buildings, as on industrial estates, the opposite is often the case, i.e. internal dividing walls are more substantial than perimeter walls.

The older multi-tenure buildings have very often been altered in some way, many having been in one occupancy to begin with. In particular, doors have been blocked up so that direct communication from one part to another no longer exists. If the job has been done well, or maybe panelled over, then you will probably not realise that this weakness exists. It is exceptionally important, therefore, to examine the wall from both sides. Even that is not a foolproof method of detection if an expert job has been done. If that wall has not been panelled or otherwise obstructed you should go through the laborious task of tapping the wall at intervals (not too far distant) in an attempt to find a different sound which will almost always mean a differing structural material. (If you go through this tapping process, cast a look over your shoulder and see the expressions on the occupants face).

Roofs have many of the problems previously mentioned i.e. maintenance, fragility, fixing etc., but in some cases are less vulnerable because of height, inaccessibility and sloping nature, causing physical hazard to the potential burglar. However, many burglars have sufficient courage to overcome these *'hazards'* as insurance claims' department staff can verify.

Probably the most common roofing materials are slates or tiles, and many surveyors seem to consider these to be strong. I find this hard to understand as, if you remove the tile or slate the best you can hope to find is timber which these same surveyors consider weak, and the removal of the slates is easy, especially in poorly maintained buildings where many literally fall off or slip, this being a virtual announcement to the burglar of an easy method of access.

Remember, if you are dealing with one section only of a multi storey, multi-occupancy building, that the ceiling and floor should be considered as similar to roofs. If your client has no control over the overall security of the building, a burglar gaining access to the floor above or below can attack your client's ceiling or floor, and this without fear of being observed from outside, as they are already in the building.

So far we have considered maintenance standards and materials but another factor can virtually override a combination of the best of these features — the location of the risk. Consider a brick or concrete walled building completely surrounded by buildings which at night are completely unmanned and with no patrol guards. Now consider a corrugated asbestos walled building with a busy road to the front and permanently manned Police Station 30 feet to the rear, with houses at either end. Which one of these two buildings would you rather insure? You see that construction, whilst important, is not a subject which can be governed by rules (though some people do try) because of other factors.

Having assessed all the factors, problems etc. concerned with the risk with which you are involved, what do you do if you are of the opinion that security requires improvement? Can you improve the physical strength of walls and roofs? Yes you can, but in the vast majority of cases the economics will rule it out as a practical proposition. The exceptions are when the area concerned is very small or, alternatively, when money is not a major consideration and that is very rare. It is conceivable to entirely line a building with welded metal mesh, but to do so you will probably have to add joists, beams, columns etc. to provide fixing points. You can add layers of bricks, concrete blocks etc. to virtually form a building within a building. However, I would suggest that any risk where this were a practical and economic proposition must have values involved of such a magnitude that it would not be handled by the trainee or novice surveyor for whom this book is intended.

It is a different situation, however, when the strengthening is required only in certain limited areas, i.e. where only a small area of the total building requires improvement. The aforementioned metal mesh, brick and concrete block are probably the most satisfactory materials to use but, as with all security measures, you must ensure proper specification and that a professional job is carried out. No exposed bolt heads, nuts or screws, whilst proper frames and intermediate supports are all essential. Bricks and blocks must be properly cemented and bonded to adjoining structures. There is little point in having good materials which, if reached, (which presumably is possible via the weak material being protected) can just be pushed aside because of incorrect or inadequate anchoring.

You will quite often encounter fairly large, comparatively weak, buildings where only a small volume of the contents are sufficiently hazardous to cause you real concern. It is, in these circumstances, complete folly to even contemplate massive physical reinforcement; far better to discuss the situation with the client and suggest a *'secure'* or *'strong'* area within the large building. You will often meet that anyway, particularly the *'stores'* part of a large workshop or garage. However, these have probably not been constructed to counter burglars but pilferers among the client's own staff. These pilferers are not expected to climb over these store walls and, consequently, the stores are often *'open topped'*, which is not effective from an anti-burglar aspect. They are also more often than not constructed of comparatively weak materials which are adequate for the purpose your client had in mind. The overall occupation is critical when considering the type of *'strong area'* to prescribe. For example, if you are worried about non ferrous metals in an engineering works it is pretty pointless suggesting a metal enclosure if there are hacksaws, boltcroppers and metal burning equipment there. In those circumstances the burglar doesn't need to bring any tools as they have been provided for him. On the other hand, such an enclosure may well be adequate if you are dealing with cigarettes, spirits or electrical goods, assuming the amount involved is appropriate.

If metal is not a suitable construction then you may have to ask for brick or concrete blocks but remember, unlike metal mesh, you cannot see through these materials so you may have to incorporate a window, especially if there is a full time stores controller to be housed in the secure area. One major problem with this type of secure area is the roof thereto. It is pointless having timber or some other weak material; that defeats the purpose of the strong walls. If you have metal, mesh or sheet, you have to be careful (as previously), about the presence of cutting or burning equipment. On one occasion I saw this latter problem countered by having several layers of metal mesh with intervening layers of rubber, the intention being that if burned, the smoke would either drive the burglar off or necessitate breathing apparatus. However, this could result in considerable smoke damage to all of the contents. The best type of ceiling is concrete but this may well need stronger walls and internal columns and beams, all adding to the cost. Any strong area, regardless of how it is constructed, must have a door, so don't neglect it in your specification for construction or your requests for improvements. The door must be of the same strength (or near as possible) as the rest of the structure, or the whole objective has been defeated.

One major problem about a *'secure area'* within a building is the fact that it is completely hidden from outsiders. If the burglar has gained entry to the main building, which we must assume is possible otherwise we wouldn't be asking for a *'secure area'*, then he, or more likely they, has all the advantages of being able to work away unobserved. You must, therefore, work on the basis that the strong area is not going to be burglar proof, but that it is buying you additional time. This bought time is only of any value if acted upon, so it follows you must have someone or something to detect the burglar whilst they are trying to gain entry into the strong area. This can be achieved, or at least attempted, in two or three different ways which will be mentioned in the next chapter.

CHAPTER 13
"Internal" Alarm Detection.

In previous chapters the more simple, or at least straightforward, items of alarm equipment were mentioned in connection with doors and windows. In the last chapter we considered physical aspects of "the building" and that now leaves us to consider alarm protection in that same respect. There should be no misunderstanding, if the value behind the walls etc is sufficient, the burglar will have little hesitation in making an attempt upon the building structure, assuming that other aspects are not favourable to him.

Wiring — This method was explained in some detail earlier and in this respect the detail is the same. This is only worth considering in relation to building protection if the area involved is quite small or the value behind the wall is exceptional. Although the materials are simple and cheap, the time involved in wiring a section of wall would be considerable and this time is very costly in terms of wages paid to the engineer concerned.

Tube and wiring — If the wall area in question is not suitable for wiring due to its construction, tube and wiring can be considered, but the considerations mentioned in the previous paragraph regarding cost apply equally here, so be careful.

Vibration Sensors — This is probably the only other type of alarm equipment which can be considered in the same light as the wiring. The idea behind these forms of detection is that the discovery will be made before the burglar is actually in the building concerned.

In limited circumstances, vibration detectors (of the varying types and principles as mentioned under doors) can be used, but once again I must stress most emphatically the problem relating to what goes on quite legitimately or accidentally (as opposed to entry attempts) outside the protected area. If there is the slightest chance of accidents etc. causing false alarms then don't use this particular equipment. Installing almost certain trouble does no good for anybody! Having given this sincere warning I must say that there are many situations where this type of equipment is exactly what is required; if so use it.

When considering the environment from an occupation, vibration and other points of view, try to visualise stormy nights. Is the building the type which might vibrate on such occasions e.g. corrugated asbestos? Try also to remember that adjoining occupancies may change, e.g. a cosmetic warehouse might become a heavy engineering factory working nightshifts. There is certainly one positive factor to vibration detection equipment in that it is probably the only type which has much chance of detecting an intruder before he makes an entry i.e. when he commences his hammer and chisel

78

work on the outside of the building or protected structure.

If you have had a *'secure area'* constructed within a main building, and assuming other factors are favourable, then vibration detectors on the secure area walls etc. may be ideal. At least in these circumstances there is more chance of the environment being controllable as the secure area is within your client's own premises. However, vibration detectors used on metal mesh *'cages'* are very accident prone, unless the cage is built to a very high specification and with a high standard of workmanship. It only takes a change in temperature to cause the metal to expand or contract sufficiently to cause vibration and an alarm condition, especially if the temperature change is quite rapid, e.g. shortly after the heating is turned off for the night. Additionally, doors or gates which do not fit tightly may *'rattle'* in a draught on a stormy night.

The following methods of detection are really intended to discover the intruder after he has actually gained entry into the building concerned.

Infra Red Rays are very thin rays of invisible light which run from a transmitter to a receiver affixed to walls, columns or some other rigid fixing point. If something crosses the path of the ray, thus interrupting the beam of light between the transmitter and the receiver, then an alarm condition is caused. This is a comparatively simple piece of equipment which in reasonable conditions causes few problems. Amongst the *'few problems'* are (1) vibration of one of the two components sufficient to cause a break in the ray, hence the necessity for very rigid fixing materials, (2) incorrect stacking of stock so that a piece of stock or something similar falls through the beam (3) incorrect stacking of stock so that the path is blocked and the alarm cannot be *'set'*, (4) birds, cats etc. passing through the path of the ray.

All of these eventualities can be *'cured'* by either good management with relation to the stock organisation, or by careful application of the equipment. If cats are a consideration, and some premises need to have them for rodent control, then the rays should be sited sufficiently high that the cats will pass beneath them and not through their path. If birds are a problem, as is often the case in warehouses with large doors through which the birds enter, then two rays can be installed, say one foot apart vertically, but wired *'in parallel'*. This means that both rays have to be broken at the same instant before an alarm condition is created. If there are birds on the premises large enough to do this then I suggest you seek advice from the nearest zoological garden!

It is obvious that these infra red rays only produce protection along the length of the very thin ray. You may, therefore, have to use several rays to form several barriers against access. Whilst this obviously achieves greater security it also places greater restrictions on the way the client can organise the contents of his building.

If you are trying to protect a *'secure area'* store it is possible to virtually form a barrier around the store by the use of many rays. The closer they are to the walls and roof the harder they are to avoid whilst trying to make an entry, and the less likely birds and cats are to cause problems.

One major snag to this equipment is that if the intruder can see the transmitter and receiver then it is not too difficult to work out the path of the ray and plan avoidance. If there are many rays it may prove a little more difficult to work out the *'pairings'*, but not too great a problem.

If the barriers are placed against (or as close as is possible to) blocked up doors, lightweight walls, windows etc, it could be considered as trying to detect entry before it has been completed as it will be hard for the criminal to avoid pieces of masonry, timber, glass etc from breaking the beams.

We now move on to what is popularly described as *'space protection'* although no-one really wants to protect, or even detect, space. However, I suppose we all know what is really being intended.

Microwave Units — The units, which are wall or vertical column mounted, are variable in size according to manufacturer, range of operation and age of production, but seldom larger than 6" x 4" x 6". Within this unit is a transmitter and receiver which are tuned to each other. The transmitter sends out radio signals at a very specific frequency which is different from **most** other common radio sources. This signal is received back by the unit receiver and, if the two signals, i.e. that transmitted and that received, are different, an alarm condition is generated. The range of the unit is the distance from the unit the manufacturer expects a human being, whilst moving at a certain speed in free space, to create sufficient disturbance to alter the radio signal to the extent of causing an alarm. This is an important principle to absorb as failure to do so can result in great problems. I repeat, the range relates to moving objects the size of a human being. Although a 20' detector should not *'see'* a human 25' away it will probably see a car, a coach or something similar at an even greater distance. Bearing that important fact in mind, read on. Microwave radio signals will penetrate glass and lightweight building materials but not brick or concrete walls. So you can imagine a 20' microwave unit looking out of a shop front 30' away is going to pick up all the passing traffic; never point a microwave at a window. A unit in a room with *'partition'* type walling from another room or a corridor, or even a door with a glass panel, may well *'see'* movement in the adjoining area. This is especially important and often neglected when considering exit routes. I have encountered cases where the keyholder has had to walk down an *'unprotected'* corridor after having set the alarm and caused false alarms by triggering microwaves in adjoining rooms through lightweight walls. In such circumstances either the unit, or the control panel, must be repositioned. The fact that glass can be penetrated by the radio waves can be an advantage as well as a disadvantage if the circumstances are right. Imagine offices with glass or part glass partitioning where ceiling entry is thought to be a problem. Depending upon the area involved you may be able to protect 2 or 3 offices with one unit and save a considerable amount of your client's money.

The unit is basically looking for movement within the area being observed. The same affect is achieved if the unit itself moves sufficiently, even if the background remains constant. It follows, therefore, that the unit must be affixed to a sound structure and not to a lightweight wall liable to vibration from outside sources.

Because of the way the radio waves move through the atmosphere, the best detection results are achieved if the intruder walks towards or away from the unit as opposed to across its face. This does not mean that cross movement or up and down (vertical) movement will never be detected, but it does mean it is more likely to escape being noticed. There are many examples of goods being lifted out through a roof without activating a microwave unit. These facts should be borne in mind, together with the most likely route of entry, when siting the unit, considering other features of the risk. What features, not already mentioned, must be remembered? Basically they fall into two categories, i.e. moving objects and surrounding objects. When you are carrying out your survey you must try and envisage ways in which the risk might develop. As an example, let us take a clothing saleshop which, when you see it, is still being *'fitted out'*. This type of shop often has mirrors for clients to look in when trying on clothing. If the mirror is angled or the unit looks at a mirror which is at an angle you may find the path looks out through a window (via the mirror) previously studiously avoided. Extensive metal lining, shelving etc. may also deflect the path in an unwanted direction. Swinging objects such as card signs, advertisements, christmas decorations, may activate the unit. Although some units are now meant to cater for this eventuality, your problem is that the unit in your premises may not have this facility or it may not be reliable. This swinging may be caused by draughts from ill fitting doors or windows or even from blower heaters operated on a time clock. The air movement is not the real problem but what does the moving air move with it? It has been known for ducted air systems to cause trouble, not because of the air but because the unit or ducting itself shuddered when the unit was automatically switched on by a time clock. Comparatively *'innocent'* things like fish tanks and plastic water pipes contain moving fish or water within materials which the unit can *'see through'*.

As mentioned under infra red rays, flying birds, often found in large warehouses, can cause terrible trouble. Although they are not *'human sized'*, they appear that way if they fly within a foot or so of the unit. These same buildings, if on modern industrial estates, may be of lightweight construction and, in stormy conditions, the whole building or a proportion of it may move or shudder in a particularly severe *'gust'* to give the required amount of movement for a false alarm to occur.

If you are trying to protect a lightweight roof it may be that cats on the outside can give trouble if the units *'field'* penetrates outside the structure itself.

Probably the most difficult problem to deal with is radio waves themselves, coming from another source altogether. Obviously you cannot see them, nor can you hear them; indeed they may not be active at the time of any survey, be it yours, or that of a specialist with correct detecting equipment. These unwanted radio signals can come from almost any unsuspected source but the most obvious are probably aircraft, emergency vehicles, taxis, radio transmitters and the like. You, as a surveyor, are almost certainly going to be in the dark with this particular problem and more often than not the problem will only be discovered by bitter experience.

The area of coverage itself must be considered. Unfortunately some people talk of *'flooding'* the area with a microwave unit. This is totally misleading. Figure 71 overleaf gives the indication of a typical area of operation of a unit but, by use of shaping devices called *'horns'*, the field can be made longer and narrower. You will see that there are corners unprotected and also areas immediately to either side of the unit itself.

There are some attempts made at "flooding" an area with several units (figure 72), but I warn you most strongly not to attempt to prescribe this form of protection unless you are being accompanied by a senior, experienced colleague. Microwaves from one unit will interfere with those from another if the two fields were to overlap. Theoretically it is possible to overcome this problem by having the units operating on different frequencies, but (a) there is no way you will know whether or not this is being done (you cannot see the frequencies) and (b) even if they are differing at the time of installation, faulty units could result in one being replaced and you cannot guarantee similar care being taken at that time. In essence, from a truly practical point of view, flooding is just not possible.

I think you will agree that nearly all rooms etc. have windows or openings of some sort, so if you try to enlarge the coverage by using a *'longer range'* unit you may cause *'penetration'*. Remember the areas covered in the diagrams are those for picking up human figures, the effective range for larger objects is greater.

Some units can change their own field of coverage due to malfunction of a component part. This could result in (a) penetration of *'see through'* materials or (b) less coverage than you think you have, either result being totally unwanted.

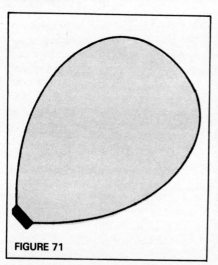

FIGURE 71

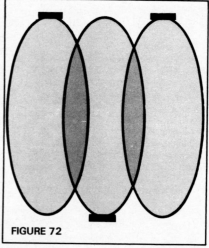

FIGURE 72

Ultrasonic Units have two major components *i.e.* the transmitter and receiver; usually they are both housed in the same unit, although some have separate housings for greater coverage. Regardless of how they are housed they all work on the same principle.

The transmitter sends out, as the unit's name suggests, ultrasound, *i.e.* sound outside the hearing range of the normal human being. This sound is at a specific frequency chosen to eliminate the vast majority of ultrasound from other sources, but it must be emphasised that no matter how sophisticated the components of the unit, not all *'unwanted'* ultrasound can be eliminated. This transmitted sound is airborne within the *'protected area'* and the receiver in the units is looking for the same frequency being returned. Any air movement will disturb the *'pattern'* looked for and cause an alarm condition. Because the sound is airborne it will not be transmitted through materials which air itself will not pass through *i.e.* glass, building materials and metal. This may give you the false impression that this type of protection is fault proof; far from it! If you think about the vast majority of buildings you have encountered, how many are *'wind proof'?* Very few I would suggest. An ill-fitting door or window, cracked glass, vent bricks etc. — there are a great many ways by which air within the building can be disturbed. The detector units are designed to accept a small amount of disturbance without activating, but obviously the tolerance must be small otherwise it soon becomes open to manipulation and would end up being installed in locations which were totally unsuitable. Because the *'signal'* is airborne, the harder the environment the better, because softness leads to absorption of the sound transmitted. You must bear this in mind when carrying out surveys, particularly if the area to be protected is empty when you see it. You may well consider that one unit will provide adequate coverage for your purposes forgetting that carpets, curtains, soft wall linings and possibly even stock (depending upon its nature *e.g.* clothing) will all absorb part of the signal transmitted, resulting in insufficient coverage being provided.

Although hard surfaces *'bounce'* the signal the amount of bounce is not great and the signal is still in a basic shape similar to a roundish balloon. You will, therefore, have unprotected areas around the rounded edges assuming a rectangular room or building. For greater coverage more units are required with differential siting, so that they do not interact, but it still remains extremely difficult to *'flood'* an area.

I previously mentioned that the transmitted ultrasound will not penetrate glass, building materials *etc.* and, whilst this is true, it does not give you a free hand to site the units anywhere you like without inviting trouble.

For best detection results the intruder should be walking towards or away from the unit as that type of movement interrupts the signal *'better'* and makes for better detection. Bearing that important factor in mind, it follows that potential or possible sources of false alarms moving towards or away from the unit are also most likely to be detected and, therefore, careful siting should avoid this possibility as much as is practicable. These two factors can, of course, provide directly opposing desires for the specifier.

If a door, for example, is the most obvious point of entry to the protected area you would initially want the unit pointing towards that door. However, that same door may be that most obvious potential interference hazard which theory says you should avoid. In such circumstances you have little alternative but to compromise and site the unit at an angle to give you the best of both worlds; not easy and perhaps an indication that different equipment should be used altogether.

It is not too difficult to imagine sources of air turbulence, *e.g.* fan heaters operated by time clocks, air conditioning plant, louvred fanlights on a stormy night etc., etc., all potential causes of false alarms, not only because of the air movement they themselves cause but because of what that air movement itself may move *e.g.* hanging signs, poorly stacked stock etc., all of which magnify the problem.

Other sources of potential false alarms obviously include unwanted ultrasound from outside the protected area. Unfortunately, this is probably the most difficult problem to assess for the surveyor who does not carry specialist detecting equipment. By its very definition you or I cannot hear ultrasound so we do not know it is present, so your only partial, and I stress partial, solution is to try and learn the more common sources of this ultrasound. These include, aircraft, steam plant, telephone bells, taxi brakes (which always seem to squeal) machinery, compressers, radio and TV transmitters and quite a few others. It is essential therefore that you *'know your patch'* and where these problems exist. The previously mentioned ill fitting doors and windows not only permit draughts on a stormy night, but the transmission of this outside ultrasound in even the calmest of conditions.

Passive Infra-red Detectors (PIR) There are two very basic points about this form of detection which must be understood from the outset, and both relate to the detector's name.

Earlier we mentioned Infra-red Rays which transmit a light beam which, when broken, causes an alarm condition. These rays have nothing to do with Passive Infra-red (PIR) detectors, they are not the same, or even similar, and should not be confused. If you encounter an alarm specification talking about *'infra-red protection'* or similar vague wording **do not accept it.** Insist upon the alarm company being more specific; is it an infra-red ray or a PIR? Unfortunately I have, not often I admit, encountered such lazy incompetent wordings.

The other basic fact to be acknowledged is that, unlike ultrasonic and microwave units, the PIR is **not** sending out any signal and during periods of *'non-detection'* it is virtually doing nothing, hence the word *'passive'* in the description of the unit.

The unit housing the equipment is roughly the same size as those containing the smaller microwave units and can easily be wall mounted in a fairly unobtrusive way.

There are basically three types of unit, the first giving a broad "layered" coverage, the second a narrow layered coverage and the third a broad flat single coverage. The first two both work on similar bases, one being for larger coverage areas and the other for narrower areas such as corridors or passageways.

In its simplest form the areas of coverage are like the fingers of a hand when spread apart and held at roughly 20° down from parallel to the ground, the fingers themselves being receptive areas and the areas between the fingers being *'dead areas'.* There are additional fingers at a greater than 20° angle from the horizontal, sited within these *'dead areas'.* Some units have a further set of fingers at an even greater angle. The first set of fingers are illustrated in figure 73, and a side view of all levels in figure 74. Whilst the actual configuration may vary slightly between various manufacturers, the basic layout will remain similar to that illustrated. The actual gaps between the

FIGURE 73   FIGURE 74

'fingers' will vary but the distance is not very large so don't be misled into thinking someone could creep up a 'dead zone' to the unit; you can't. In any case, in a good unit the 'lower' fingers would fill the gaps left by the upper fingers.

The third version has only one finger (yet finger is probably the worst way to try and describe it — it is more like a sheet of paper, thin and broad). Because of its shape it is becoming more and more commonly accepted as a prime method of protecting large areas of glass, the unit being placed approximately 12″ inside the window concerned. A favourite location is for shop fronts, but care should be exercised with the siting of the unit. PIR's do not have the ability to see through glass, timber etc, this being an advantage in many, many instances. However, it is also a cause for care to be exercised as the relationship between any door and the unit siting could be critical. This is explained further in the last two paragraphs of this section.

What are the receptive fingers looking for, remembering there is no transmission from the unit itself? They are looking for infra-red energy. Virtually every material with a surface temperature greater than absolute zero ($-273°C$) radiates infra-red energy to some degree or other. In a still condition, everything within a room or building will be emitting a steady flow of such energy which the unit 'sees', memorises and considers acceptable. However, a sudden change in this steady flow, such as the introduction of a new body (human or otherwise) of sufficient size to disturb this flow will not be considered acceptable and an alarm condition will be created. A human being cannot (as far as I am aware) just materialise, he must come from somewhere and it is his passage between the receptive rays which registers in the unit. Because the unit is more receptive to someone crossing the various rays as opposed to walking up a ray towards the unit, best results are obtained if the unit is sited with that in mind, thinking of the most likely routes of an intruder's entry. This, you will realise, is directly opposed to the theory for microwaves and ultrasonic units.

Because the unit is looking for an increase in infra-red energy as produced by a human being it is fairly obvious that similar increases from other sources

85

will cause false alarms. Heating units which heat up rapidly are a prime example, especially if they are time clock controlled to *'come on'* after the alarm has been set. Direct sunlight shining into the unit suddenly, is another.

One obvious question often asked is *"what if the burglar conceals himself in a suit, mask etc. so as to conceal his entire person — will the alarm still detect him"?* Manufacturers usually say *"yes as the suit, mask etc. itself will generate infra-red energy sufficient to cause an alarm"*. I have no way to prove or disprove this theory but have heard sufficient comment to raise doubts in my mind. However, I have rarely heard of burglars behaving in such a manner outside of cinema productions. If you do have fears in this connection because of the degree of risk involved, consideration must be given to alternative or supplementary detection devices.

Mention was made earlier of long thin detection fields designed for corridors and the like. These quite often comprise only one finger or maybe two or three on a vertical as opposed to a horizontal plane. Because the field of coverage is comparatively thin it follows that if someone can by-pass this *'narrow'* protection the detection purposes of the unit may have been defeated. Consider what would happen if a door was opened across the detector's field of vision, someone then came through the doorway with the door between him and the detector. It is then conceivable for him to have crossed the path of the detector having been shielded and undetected. This does not imply any criticism of the equipment but emphasises the necessity for proper siting and use.

Bear this in mind when relating to shop front protection. If the door were to be opened by false keys or the like, the door could shield the intruder from the unit.

Dual Sensor Units — These units are now appearing on the market and being used with increased frequency by installers. What are they?. Well, in simple terms they are two detectors in one housing unit, the detectors working on completely differing principles. As far as I am aware there is always a PIR involved and the other unit will be either an ultra sonic unit or a microwave. I have not heard of the combination of these latter two detection forms in the same unit as the problems they face have too many similarities.

The whole concept is anything but new. Many years ago there were combined ultra sonic/microwave units, but they never caught on.

The thinking behind these units is sound and difficult to argue against, not that I want to anyway. There are many situations where the conditions are just not suitable for any PIR, microwave or ultra sonic unit, there being something in the set up which is a snag to each, but the snags may not be common to all units. Let me try to explain further. Assume that a room has something which affects ultra sonic units; and another problem which affects PIR's, but specific problems of the one type of unit do not affect the other type of unit. It follows therefore that if you install both of these pieces of equipment **and** have them working together, and that is the vitally important point, then unless the two snags work at exactly the same split second there will be no false alarm as only one piece of the equipment will activate and the lack of activity from the other unit will ensure that there is no false alarm, as both units must trigger simultaneously to create an alarm condition.

As you know false alarms are a scourge, and if this development goes a long way to eliminating some of these calls, then it must be good. As you would imagine these units are more expensive than single units and that is only right and to be expected. It should go without saying, but regrettably does not, that due to the increased expense these units should only be used when the circumstances deserve, and not with the attitude that their installation might solve something which has never been investigated to see if it exists. I have experienced exactly that happening, but far be it from me to even suggest that increased profit could have had anything to do with the action taken.

General Comments

There are certain very important points which must be borne in mind and which relate to microwave, ultra sonic and passive infra red detector units.

Their stated range and area of coverage is intended for *'ideal conditions'* and I do not know where they exist outside of the laboratory or at specially prepared exhibitions. I have certainly never met such perfection in commercial situations and I would suggest that you will be a very lucky person if you do. This is not intended as a criticism of the manufacturers, there is no way they can forsee all of the varieties of potential problems to be encountered and then produce information which would be intelligible and useful to potential users.

In an attempt to try and cater for some of these problems a form of adaptability has been inbuilt in that the range of many units is manually adjustable. Now that sounds fine, and in theory it is fine, but, yes there is always a but, this ability to adjust can be, and regrettably is (by the less scrupulous) used for the wrong purposes. Let us imagine that a particular unit is causing false alarms and it is not easy to see the reason. One of the first instincts is to reduce the unit's range to see if that solves anything. Quite often it does the trick, there being something in the environment which is the root of the trouble, but which is not covered if the range reduction is maintained. The false alarm problem may well be solved, but what degree of security is left?, how far was the range reduced to accomplish the miracle cure?. What should have happened, of course, is that the problem source be identified and either (i) removed, or if that is not practical (ii) other alternative equipment installed in place of that which was not suitable. Whatever happened, the security should not have been reduced. The Dual Sensor Units have been introduced to cater for some of these eventualities, but even they can be adjusted so the units are still open to manipulation.

As indicated in the description relating to each of these pieces of equipment, they are, to put it simply, looking at space and awaiting an intrusion into that space. If you remove, or greatly impair, the ability to see the space, obviously you reduce the ability of the unit concerned to operate properly. It will surprise you how often you will find just that happening, the most common sources of the problem being the placing of stock in the incorrect place, erection of fittings, or the erection of partitioning too close to the unit. As far as I am concerned there is no excuse for this. If the client was not aware that what he was doing was going to impair the efficiency, then the

Installer is at fault for not having explained the potential problem at the time of installation. If he did explain the facts to the client at the time of the installation and the client has not passed them on to the staff concerned, then quite clearly the client is at fault. The point that I am trying to make is that the equipment, in this case, did not malfunction, it did what it should do, the fault is purely human. The more likely reason is that the client just did not think, or care. I often wonder what the attitude of an Insurer would be if a loss were to occur in these circumstances, the unit and alarm is operational, but not in the manner intended or the manner in which the Insurer thought it was when cover was granted.

I have seen claims made that areas have been completely covered by using space detection units, where in fact there has been nothing like complete coverage. Active units, eg microwave and ultra sonic, actually send out transmissions as previously explained. If the fields of these transmissions overlap with another from a similar device they can react with each other and cause false alarms. Some claims are made that the units are operating on differing frequencies so that this problem will not arise, but neither you nor I can check this, and if it were as easy as is said, I would have expected to see it done much more often than actually occurs. Because of this, I do not treat such claims seriously. It is possible to have infra red units (passive) overlapping as they do not transmit and therefore there is nothing to interact. However, even with them, to get complete coverage would necessitate an awful lot of units, probably making it uneconomical.

In a previous chapter we mentioned *'secure areas'* and that, in effect, they only bought time. This purchase is only of use if it is used wisely and not squandered. I do not advise automatic use of *'space detection'* in these areas for 2 reasons (i) the secure area has to be pierced before the detectors will be effective, therefore some of the bought time has been wasted, and (ii) these secure areas are often quite small (having been built specially at some cost) and the area available will make the operation of most of the detectors very difficult to achieve. Far better to have the detection equipment outside, looking at the secure area, so that the intruder is picked up before making his entry to the area in question.

The problems and false alarms sources are well known to unit manufacturers and installers and have been for several years now. Over the years there have obviously been refinements and improvements but manufacturers have achieved these in differing degrees and using different methods. The surveyor is placed in the unfortunate position of having to rely solely on *'other people's say so'* as to whether the equipment about to be used in any specific case can cope with known, comparatively minor, aspects regarding interference. Until the day comes when there is equipment testing, evaluation, or call it what you will, the surveyor is at a distinct disadvantage and I can offer only two solutions to this problem, (a) only use installers you know very well and know you can trust to tell you the truth and not sell you trouble or, (b) assume the worst and design your protection accordingly.

The novice surveyor (and experienced surveyors for that matter) can have another problem not really appreciated by many, especially the expert manufacturer or installer. The housings of many units have some remarkable similarities, and just looking at the box on the wall can leave some people slightly confused, to put it mildly. This problem would not arise were alarm specifications always present and accurate, but alas that is very seldom the case. This is obviously a plea for some form of identification. Good grief!, I can hear the screams of horror from where I am sitting now. "That would be an aid to the intruder", I hear you say. Question — do burglars arm themselves differently, or change their methods depending upon the form of space protection present?. I would suggest that if we are encountering that sort of burglar with that degree of sophistication it will take a lot more than confusing boxes to baffle him; you are talking about the "real pro's".

I find it hard to believe that, with modern science being widely used by the manufacturers anyway, they cannot come up with something a little bit more identifiable. Remember, dear manufacturer, we are not only dealing with your products, but with those of your competitors (do I hear someone say "that is not our problem"?, surely not). Help!

Consideration has been given to 'space protection' by means of ultra sonic, microwave and passive infra red detectors. The fact that there is a choice should mean that, for the vast majority of cases, reasonable security should be possible with relatively reduced occasions where false alarms occur. Each type of detector has its advantages and disadvantages, but it should, in theory, be possible to produce a list of 'yes and no' for each type of equipment and each potential cause of false alarm, indeed Table 1 overleaf attempts to do just that with some qualifications.

Some manufacturers produce similar tables, but I would remind you that (a) they are assuming that each piece of equipment is installed 100% accurately and in strict accordance with their instructions (how do we surveyors know whether or not this is the case?), and (b) as well as being manufacturers they are also out to sell their product. I am in no position to say that their claims are inaccurate. If you examine some of the lists produced by the manufacturers you will soon find out that they do not all say the same things about the various pieces of equipment. Now that does not necessarily mean that any of them are being untruthful, it probably means that there is such a variety of equipment available that to be definitive about the pros and cons is impossible. The lists that they produce usually refer to currently produced equipment, but you will undoubtedly come across older equipment and the same pros and cons will probably not apply due to progress having changed the entire situation. Development of 'space detectors' is probably one of the most rapid in the security industry and, for that reason, if for no other, if you have any doubts at all as to what piece of equipment should be used in any particular situation, you have no choice but to make exacting enquiries of the installer as to just what he intends to use.

It follows from the foregoing that the information in Table 1 must, I repeat, must only be taken as guidelines and cannot in any way be considered as being 'gospel'. However, the questions etc. might put you on the right path as to what you should be looking for, both in circumstances and in equipment.

There are three further points on which I would give some cautionary notes, viz (i) The development of equipment does not mean that all equipment you will encounter will have the latest 'good points', there are still

TABLE 1

Affected by		Answer
General increase in temperature	MWD	Not usually, unless the source of the increase is sudden and causes movement of, or within, the heat generator.
	US	Not usually a major problem.
	PIR	If the general temperature reaches the body temperature, an intruder might not be detected.
Susceptibility to extreme heat or cold	MWD	Most units have operational temperature limits. Few are really effective below freezing point. Could be a major problem in warehouse risks which are unheated.
	US	
	PIR	
Vibration of unit	MWD	Can be a severe problem.
	US	Can be a problem.
	PIR	Not normally a problem unless the movement is severe.
Air movement within the protected area	MWD	Can be a problem if the air in turn moves other items.
	US	Can be a problem if the air movement causes ultrasound.
	PIR	Not normally a problem.
Penetration through glass and other lightweight building materials	MWD	A severe problem.
	US	Not normally a problem unless ultrasound from outside the protected area can 'penetrate in'. ̶g̶ ̶i̶i̶ ̶t̶i̶a̶.̶.̶.̶.̶
	PIR	Not normally a problem.
Distorted field of cover by deflection off metal	MWD	Can be a severe problem.
	US	Not normally a problem. which is sited with̶ ̶̶
	PIR	̶ ̶ ̶ ̶ ̶p̶rotect̶
Absorption by fabrics etc.	MWD	Not normally a problem.
	US	Can be a severe problem.
	PIR	Not normally a problem.
Susceptible to small animals.	MWD	Problem is small animals get too close to the unit. Careful siting should avoid this problem.
	US	
	PIR	
Heaters, radiators and the like	MWD	Not normally a problem unless they are fan assisted and operate whilst the alarm is 'set'
	US	Not normally a problem unless the units produce ultrasound and this is not usual.
	PIR	Can be a bad problem if the units are badly sited in relation to the heaters.
Moving objects, e.g. fan blades, signs and Christmas decorations	MWD	Can be a major problem.
	US	Can be a problem if not properly sited.
	PIR	Not normally a problem.
Sunlight or car headlights directly or deflected onto the unit	MWD	Not normally a problem.
	US	
	PIR	Can be a severe problem.
Water moving in plastic pipes	MWD	Major problem.
	US	Not a problem.
	PIR	Not a problem.
Noise, sonic and ultra sonic	MWD	Not normally a problem.
	US	A major problem.
	PIR	Not a problem.
Interference between units of the same type	MWD	Definite problem.
	US	Definite problem.
	PIR	Not a problem.
Range Fluctuation (accidental e.g. by environment, age, etc.)	MWD	Yes.
	US	Yes.
	PIR	Yes.
Adjustable range (intentional)	MWD	Yes.
	US	Yes.
	PIR	No.

hundreds of older pieces out there amongst your clients, (ii) the dual sensor detectors are not included in the table, but you should, to all intents and purposes, treat them as two separate pieces of equipment from the point of view of deciding their suitability, (iii) if you encounter equipment in circumstances where you think there is a distinct potential problem, query the fact with the installer, it could be that the problem source was not there when the equipment was installed, or it might be the installer is of the opinion that he is using equipment which has had that potential problem catered for by some magical means. If this is asserted to you, do not be afraid to ask for a brochure which points this out and, if there is any hesitancy about providing this, it might just raise some doubts in your mind about the truth of the matter.

CHAPTER 14
Alarm Controls & Signalling

We have now dealt with the most commonly used detection devices. However, just because these devices have activated it is only part of the problem; what happens as a consequence is equally important, so that is where we now progress.

It is not very easy to explain the happenings after a detection device has activated without getting too bogged down in technical detail, and that is not the purpose of a book aimed at novice surveyors. You will however, I hope, accept that it is pointless to have a detection device activating if that is the end of the story!

Each detection device is connected to a control panel within the protected premises, although it is not always within a protected area within the protected premises, there being quite a difference between the two. This connection is made by means of electric wiring of a specific type and design. It is thicker and more complex than the wiring used for protecting timber doors and similar items, but it has two things in common therewith. One is that, in a way, it is part of the detection devices in that if cut or damaged it will create an alarm condition, so that tampering with the wiring is considered the same as tampering with a door contact, for instance. The other similarity is that it has been made complex (just as the more modern door wire pattern has) in an effort to beat attempts to *'loop out'* etc.

Because damaged wiring can cause an alarm condition, the routing of this wiring must be carefully considered bearing in mind the occupancy, and if conditions are such that heavy stock or portable machinery or the like could have the potential to cause such damage then the wiring should either be re-routed away from this hazard or, alternatively, be physically protected, usually by running it through metal tubing which is then secured to the building structure. A point worth looking for during resurveys is whether the wiring is still firmly attached to the walls or other fixing as, if some staples have worked loose and the wire is hanging free, it is more easily damaged. It is also an idea to ask the client how long it has been in that condition; the answer you get may reveal several things, *e.g.* (a) he hasn't even noticed it before, so obviously doesn't look out for potential problems, (b) it has been that way for a while but he hasn't done anything about it, so he doesn't care about his system, (c) it has been that way for a while but the Alarm Company maintenance engineer didn't seem to worry about it, indicating possible poor maintenance standards which could also apply to the remainder of the system.

The number of separate wires running into the alarm control box depends upon many things. A *'circuit'* is the term used for the wire run connecting several detection devices onto the one cable and back to the control panel. It is quite possible, from an electrical ability point of view, to have dozens of detection devices all connected up to any one of the wires in the cable running back to the control panel, **but** it is highly undesirable. To do so means that fault finding and good maintenance is virtually an impossibility, because the engineer just doesn't know where to start looking for the trouble; the problem could be anywhere along the length of that particular wire. Unfortunately, there are installers who perpetrate this undesirable practice but I am glad to say they are a dying breed; however, you will doubtless enccunter old systems where this situation still exists. Indeed, not very long ago I found an old system with yards of tube and wiring, door wiring, door contacts, ultrasonic units and window vibration detectors all on a single circuit. Needless to say that system was giving trouble and had to be totally replaced. It is not possible for me to tell you here how many detectors should be on one circuit, it all depends on the premises and the system components and design. The basic considerations are those of fault finding, by the engineer trying to rectify problems and by the client trying to set the system at night. Try putting yourself in their position and if you reckon you could not cope, what reason have you for assuming others can? Obviously, from a technical point of view, you must be guided by the installer but from a purely practical aspect use your own imagination. There are restrictions regarding maximum numbers of detectors in one circuit imposed by BS 4737 (refer to your copy for up to date information), but that does not mean the maximum must be used.

Now that we have the detectors connected via wiring to the control box let us consider that latter piece of equipment itself. The range and variety is quite enormous and it is in this field that probably the most development has been taking place in recent years. In the *'old days'* all detectors were connected on one circuit to a single circuit panel. With the development and extension of more sophisticated detection devices, the single circuit control box was considered by many (except the more foolish previously mentioned) to be so inadequate that a more complex control box was required for the more extensive, complicated alarm systems. These complex control boxes proved to be inappropriate and too costly for some systems which were beyond single circuit but had not reached the complicated stage, so there was a development of *'in between'* control boxes. This resulted in installers having to keep a *'range'* of control boxes which was not really economic. Fortunately, the microchip appeared on the scene resulting in the possibility of having control boxes which could be adapted for virtually any set of circumstances and, at the same time, there was a drive to make them simple to operate. Personally, I have mixed feelings on this latter subject. If you make a system too easy can it not lead to complacency and lack of interest on the part of the operator? If it does, surely this cannot be good for overall security? Some people want control boxes which are *'idiot proof'*, myself I don't want idiots in charge of alarm systems!

What is the purpose of the control box? It enables the client to switch the system *'on'* or *'off'* and, in addition, there is a *'test'* facility whereby the system is turned on *except* for the signalling devices (more on these later) and allows the user to test the detection devices to see if they are working or not. If this facility were used more often by clients it would get rid of much antagonism which exists between the client and his installer. Because the testing is seldom used, many, many, systems only show the faults and problems when *'closing up'* time arrives, so the user, in common with others with the same attitude, contacts his installer expecting immediate rectification service. As the majority of businesses close within an hour or so of each other you can probably imagine the problem facing installers. If the system had been tested sometime during the day it may well have shown up the fault at that time and the maintenance engineer could be summoned then, instead of waiting until everyone else wants him at the same time. You may be asking yourself *'what has this got to do with me? Surely that is the client's problem'.* If you are I suggest you give up surveying right now; you are part of a service industry and part of your service is to help your client in any reasonable way you can, and if that means educating him (even if someone else should be, but has failed to do so) then so be it, get on with it.

Obviously, not all detectors can be tested to see if they are working, *e.g.* foil tape, tube and wiring and vibration detectors, but testing might reveal broken connections, loose fittings *etc.* Door contacts can be tested simply by opening the door, and *'space protection'* by walking into the protected zone and seeing if the small light on the detector operates or not, and at what range it operates. Because of the way in which space protection is *'set up'* this can be *'walk tested'* even when the system is switched off. This latter *'ability'* causes some people concern as in certain circumstances it means potential intruders can *'case the joint'* and test the field whilst posing as customers etc. If this does concern you, you can have the units amended so that the walk testing can only be carried out when the controls are in the test condition.

How are the faults etc. shown at the control box? With controls with more than one circuit there is a separate small light for each circuit, and if the light is lit up when the alarm is *'on'* then there is a fault in that circuit, although with some systems a button must be pushed, or something similar, before this light will show. In single circuit controls there is only one light to cover the entire detection system. These lights serve a dual purpose as they will also light up if a detection unit is activated after the system has set, thus indicating where the fault has subsequently arisen or which detection circuit has been tripped by an intruder. Assuming the indicator lights are not faulty and the alarm activates without a circuit light illuminating that, in all probability, indicates a fault has arisen either in the control box itself or in the remote signalling (explained later) if applicable, or possibly even the external bell. So the absence of an indicator lamp in these circumstances is, in effect, an indication of the location of the trouble.

The alarm controls should be sited within the protected area to detect anyone trying to attack them and immobilise the system. However, if this is done then it follows that after setting the alarm system in an *'on'* condition, the keyholder must pass through either a protected area or door, or something, unless he stays there all night. To cater for this, one of two methods are used. (a) A time delay whereby the operator has to vacate the protected area within a certain specified time and, having done so, either turn a key in a lock, depress a button or something similar in equipment connected to the alarm system, thus indicating correct exit procedure. The opposite operation has to take place on opening up the next day. (b) A lock in the final exit door is connected into the alarm system and, when the key is turned, it *'sets'* the detection devices in the exit route. There may be variations on these themes which, if encountered, should be examined for yourself.

Another facility in some control boxes which causes controversy in certain circles is the presence of isolation switches. These are switches which, when operated, permit certain circuits to be *'left off'* when the rest of the system is *'on'*. There are circumstances where this facility is perfectly justifiable and proper, *e.g.* in a system where, for business operation reasons, it is desirable that certain vacated areas are protected, whilst other areas, where late work is continuing, are left unset. The snags are that (a) the late workers may forget to switch their portion *'on'* and leave them unprotected or (b) if a fault in a circuit is discovered at locking up time there is a temptation to leave that area unprotected and set the rest rather than wait for an engineer to arrive. Is it better to have a partial system rather than none at all, or do you want to create a system where the keyholder is tempted to leave the entire system *'off'*? There are pros and cons to every argument and your own employer may have specific rules on topics such as this — find out.

We have so far covered detection devices and control panels but, even with these connected to each other, we are far from having a complete alarm system.

The next stage is *'what makes the system work'* i.e. what powers it. From previous comments you will have gathered it is electricity, but from where? The most usual method is from the public mains, but within the control box there is equipment to regulate the supply which can be very erratic in its power. Although such erratic nature may not be obvious to you it is very noticeable to comparatively delicate, finely tuned, electronic equipment. Without this regulating feature the alarm equipment would be subject to surges and lapses which would play havoc with the system and cause many false alarms. This regulated electricity flows through the whole system, but because of distance of detectors (mainly volumetric) from the controls, there may be such a loss of power through the cable itself that there is insufficient power left by the time it reaches these detectors. Where this does occur the power at these detectors has to be supplied or boosted by the use of batteries. Full mains power would also be far too strong for the delicate alarm equipment (it has to be delicate to perform to its optimum capabilities), so also within the control panel there is yet more equipment to reduce this power to an acceptable level. Batteries are also required at the control unit to cater for occasions where the public mains supply fails for whatever reason. They are so arranged that, to all intents and purposes, the instant the mains power fails the battery power takes over. Because of the potential reliance on battery power it is fairly obvious that the standard of batteries used must be of the highest calibre or disaster is imminent. Those within, or close by, the controls must be rechargeable to maintain the high standard of alertness, whilst those remotely positioned for space detectors must be constantly maintained. The actual operating performances of the batteries are specifically laid down in BS 4737 to which you should refer for up-to-date details.

There is not much point in having detection devices, controls etc. if no-one is going to know when the system works properly. It is obvious, therefore, that we must have some sort of cry for help, i.e. signalling. The degree of signalling required obviously depends upon several factors and these will vary from risk to risk.

I know that some people lay down grades of risk for which differing signalling methods are required. Personally, apart from the extremes of the spectrum of risks, and even this may be doubtful, I do not see how this can be done. There are so many variable factors and combinations thereof that it is just not practicable to be systematic in grading.

All I intend doing in this connection is mention some of the factors which might influence your decision, but not in any order of importance.

1. The attractiveness of the risk itself is fairly obvious. Highly re-sellable domestic electric goods are more likely to be stolen than flowers. What is attractive to a burglar changes quite often with fashion, technology, price, scarcity and transportability. High value in small volume also makes a collection of objects more attractive than high value in large volume.

2. The actual volume of the attraction and its value. You may well have a small quantity of something quite valuable in amongst a large volume of less attractive goods, making it harder to find to steal.

3. Is the presence of attractive goods on the premises well known? It is obvious a spirit warehouse contains vast quantities of spirits, but it may not be well known that a boardroom has a safe, a cocktail cabinet and a TV.

4. How easy is it to mount an alarm bell, externally, in such a position that it is not easily attacked and removed? If that is a problem, do you need something else in addition?

5. How close to the risk is there any human habitation, guards, night workers etc., in other words people who are likely to hear alarm bells ringing? When thinking of this remember prevailing winds on a stormy night, other noise sources e.g. close proximity of a major airport. I always feel it is unwise to rely on guards in a neighbouring factory etc. Your client has no control of that risk and may not know when the guarding arrangements have been cancelled.

6. Are the people in close proximity the type of person to co-operate and act upon the bells ringing, or are they more likely to be the people perpetrating the burglary? It is an unpleasant fact which must be accepted that large sections of the population are just not co-operation minded and *'just do not want to get involved'.* In that kind of location, are alarm bells going to serve any purpose?

7. If you do want remote signalling (explained later) then you must ask yourself why you want it? Depending on your answer will depend the type of remote signalling required. Is it just because bells ringing will not be heeded or is it because the risk itself is sufficiently hazardous to warrant remote signalling regardless of the local inhabitants?

These are only some of the factors which will influence your decision. There are far too many (some of them you may only encounter once or twice) for me to list. I would, however, stress that you must consider your decision very carefully; not only is your risk involved, so too is your client's money if you ask for more than the risk warrants.

The following are the various forms of signalling which are commonly used.

Audible Only

This type of signalling used to be referred to as *'Bells only'*, and in many cases still is, but with the development in use of sirens the terminology is changing. This is probably the most common signalling system which is still used extensively, is certainly the cheapest form available, yet still not all that cheap. Despite being the oldest form of signalling, modern devices bear little resemblance (at least operationally) to the earlier versions. Even the appearance and materials for bell housings have changed in recent years and will no doubt change more in the future. It used to be the case that all housings were metal, but polycarbonates are used extensively now. BS 4737 lays down criteria, but is delightfully vague in saying words to the effect that *'polycarbonate must be of equivalent strength to metal housings'* but, as far as I know, no tests etc have been devised to prove the relative strengths. The old box shape has also been overtaken to some extent by a variety of shapes, some being likened to air fresheners. No proving tests by independent persons have been undertaken to prove whether or not one is better than another. To comply with BS 4737, the bell must be *self activating (or actuating)'*. This means that the bell must contain its own power source (a battery), and be so designed and installed that, if attacked and removed, it will continue to operate even if the burglar is running down the road with it under his arm. Personally, I do not accept that they are all designed to a similar standard. I think that some are much easier to attack and overcome than others, but one lone voice will not change matters. The usual reply one receives is *"it hasn't happened'* (ie attacks by dismantling boxes), a phrase I often hear in many spheres. However, I thought we were trying to be ahead of the burglar, not behind him!

If a bell does not comply to BS 4737, as is the case with many DIY and *'non approved'* systems, then the removal of the bell from the wall may well mean the silencing of the entire system. Useless!

As losses prove, it is fairly easy to overcome even a BS 4737 bell. They all have some form of *'opening'* to let out the sound. If they didn't the sound would not travel very far. Into these holes, liquid plastic materials can, and are, pumped, left to harden, and completely silence the bell. These methods of attack reinforce the argument that the bell should be as inaccessible as possible, without stifling the actual bell sound. However, this could lead to a lack of maintenance by engineers. You can't win.

If you cannot make the bell inaccessible, you may have to consider the use of more than one bell, so that one being attacked would trigger off another.

A recent development is the *'bell cut out'*, and this has raised a mountain of controversary in insurance circles without any definitive attitude being pronounced by the Insurance Industry collectively.

What happens is that in the control box, not the bell itself, a piece of equipment, probably yet another micro chip, is installed, which has the effect of *'switching off the bell'* after a predetermined period, usually 20 minutes. This has arisen because of complaints about bells ringing for, literally, hours without any attention being paid to them. Keyholding response is obviously at the root of this problem. In some cases Local Bye Laws insist upon these cut outs being installed at the time of installation, whilst others only after there have been complaints about the lengthy bell ringing. You should acquaint yourselves with the situation in the areas where you operate, although I wouldn't be surprised if the compulsory installation is upon us in all areas before long. Until that situation is with us, what do we face? In my opinion little short of shambles. Alarm Installer's Specifications vary enormously in many respects, none more so than this. Is the cut out installed? Is it installed but not connected? (in some cases the equipment is automatically installed but not connected until required — an easy 10 second job). A large proportion of Specifications make no mention at all or, at best, unclear mention, but that does not help us either.

Coming with many of these cut outs is the ever increasing *'flashing light'*. This is a light, built into or onto the bell cover. In some cases it operates at the time the bell rings, and in others after the bell has ceased ringing. There are arguments for flashing lights in the following circumstances (1) in a multi tenure building with many alarm bells, where it allows the Police to identify which bell is ringing, (2) in a very dark street, possibly tree lined, where it is difficult to identify quickly where the bell is ringing.

What are the disadvantages of cut outs and flashing lights. Well I think that they must include the following:— (a) they let the burglars know that the system has been activated, allow them to observe what the response and activity is, ie, it is an aid to their planning an attack. (b) unless the system is of the type which re-sets after the cut out period has elapsed (there are some, but it is doubtful whether the specification will say so), the burglar knows that a subsequent attack will provoke no further action. I know that this can all be done to a system without cut outs or flashing lights, but I see no attributes in helping the burglar any more than we have to. What is your employer's attitude? — you don't know, well find out, quickly.

The other device used for Audible Alarm signalling is the Siren, not common, but still present and possibly increasing. Basically, it is a device which makes a lot more (different) noise than the traditional bell. The noise, as well as being different, is a lot more piercing, and likely to penetrate other noises such as wind and other bells. They are, therefore, used where bells are considered not adequate. The disadvantages are (a) I believe that there are as yet no *'self activating'* models on the market, consequently they are easy to silence and remove, (b) if people are going to complain about the traditional bell noise, they are going to go completely bonkers at siren noise. I know of one case where the sirens had to be removed due to complaints by neighbours, yet not on one occasion did the complainants ring the Police to advise of a possible intrusion, only to complain. (c) I know of no specification for sirens, so what is being used?. I think the main advantage is the ability of the *'noise'* to travel further.

One last point on bells. I think that there is little argument that bells are being more and more ignored by Joe Public, regardless of the type of location.

Remote Signalling
999 Autodiallers are a mechanical attempt to replace you, the human being. When you have a *'Bells only'* system, you rely upon a member of the public dialling 999 to summon the Police.

A system said to be on a 999 basis has a piece of equipment intended to do this work instead of relying on Joe or Joanne Public. I have no intention of going into the cogs, spindles and woofers involved, I do not think that is necessary. The intention is that when an intrusion happens, the magic box springs into action, dials 999, just as you do, and then transmits a pre-recorded message which has been stored on a tape, cassette or record within the machinery. Now just let's think of what we are expecting to happen.

(a) Machinery which may have been lying idle for months, or even years, to work perfectly. A tape held under some tension may snap when asked to move. The same tape might stick to the equipment that it has been held against for a long period. Dust, dirt or grit may distort the message even if the equipment does work. The record arm might *'jump'* and miss part of the message, at the same time scratching the record to botch up future transmissions. If the equipment does work, but at the wrong speed, the message might be unintelligible.

(b) The machinery is to do the same as you, so it faces the same problems, ie no dialling tone, wrong number, noisy lines etc, etc. The big difference is that you know what is happening and can try again, the machinery can't think, so if it is unsuccessful, hard luck, it won't try again, you've had it. True you will probably have a bell back up, but if you were happy to rely on bells, why have you asked for a 999?

Apart from having machinery which is very prone to error, you are also relying upon a telephone line which has nothing special about it at all. In a very large number of cases, the line is draped along the building wall and disappears through a hole in a door or window frame. Even if your premises are high above ground level, the line will probably come down the wall, and if you are very lucky, it will go behind a piece of thin metal which is poorly attached to the wall, at a height of approx 8', not too high for a reasonably determined crook. If the line is within reach it is easy to break by hand or cut with a pair of scissors — result, no 999. An argument often put forward is that it very seldom happens, and that is true, but are you prepared to be the exception that proves the rule? One way of countering this problem is to have the line enter the premises underground. Great, if it is done properly. I have seen a case where the line was brought down the wall, a hole made in the pavement, the line taken into the basement and back up to the autodialler. The line did come in underground, but was still exposed on the external wall. If you say that it must go underground to the first telegraph pole it will depend on where that pole is as to whether that is good enough. If it is close to the premises, it doesn't take a genius to work out that that is probably going to be the pole concerned, and the line will probably go up the side of the pole easily within reach. A further stage is to say the 2nd closest telegraph pole, when you could be talking about considerable distances. The costs involved in doing this kind of work are quite horrendous. It would be better to ask for a higher grade of signalling which could be cheaper.

Let us assume that you are lucky and have a secure line, but you still have all the potential trouble of (a) and (b) above.

The line to the signalling equipment could be engaged if someone were to 'call in' prior to breaking in; the line being busy the '999' cannot make contact. To overcome this you should always ask for the line involved to be 'outward going calls only'. This means that calls can only go in the one direction, and no-one can intentionally engage the line. It is common practice to also ask for the line to be ex-directory, ie the number does not appear in any telephone directory, nor should any telephone operator give it over in 'enquiries'. If the line is outgoing only, I can't really see the need for this latter request as, even if someone knows the number, what can he do?. If the fear is that of a British Telecom worker getting to know and overcoming it in the exchange, I feel that he could probably obtain that information anyway.

Although I have never experienced it myself, I believe that it is possible, or was possible, to have a switch attached to the phone equipment which enables the line to be 'normal' during the day, so that the subscriber can have full use thereof. I don't like this idea, as, sure as fate, the switch will be forgotten some night and it will be then that a loss will occur.

Unfortunately, British Telecom insist that with each 999 unit there must be a normal telephone instrument, even if there is no intention to use the line normally. If this is not kept isolated it can be 'knocked off the hook', thus stopping the call from being made. There is an advantage to having a handset etc, ie, the line can be checked regularly to see that it is operational, but I doubt if that is ever done.

From the time that the signal is instigated by an alarm happening, there is a lapse of some 30 seconds before the message actually starts being transmitted. Add to that the time to transmit enough of the message to be identifiable, and you will appreciate that this means that the actual unit must be fairly secure, otherwise a heavy hammer could stop any further action.

I am not a fan of this type of equipment, but accept that there is a place for it, but few.

Digital Dialler (not to be confused with a Digital Communicator) There is a lot of confusion between a Digital Dialler and a Digital Communicator, due to the fact that when Digital Communicators were first developed they were indeed called Digital Diallers.

A Digital Dialler is still a 999 signaller, only the method of operation of the actual equipment has moved on from the older versions and is done 'digitally', which in turn means that the operation is quicker and probably more reliable in terms of dialling the correct number.

However, there is no doubt in my mind that if the terms are being used correctly, a Digital Dialler is still only a 999 and must have virtually all the same pros and cons referred to earlier.

Digital Communicators (not to be confused with Digital Diallers). This is yet another comparatively recent development in alarm signalling, but it is spreading in use exceptionally quickly, and currently is probably the most commonly used form of remote signalling. It is more costly to install than a 999 but, in my opinion, the increased cost is more than outweighed by the increased efficiency. However, that does not infer in any way that it is the be all and end all in signalling. Far from it, there are deficiencies.

Once again, the public switched network is used, ie the normal telephone lines that we all use for everyday calls. It follows that some of the flaws mentioned under 999 signalling in this connection still remain. The main problem is still the *'cut line'*. If it is cut then no message gets through to the Central Station of which more will be mentioned later. However, *'additions'* can be made which do improve the situation, but do not restore it to full efficiency as when the line is intact. There is, however, as much confusion over these *'additions'* as the equipment itself, primarily because of name similarity.

The effect these additions have are:—

(i)   when the line is cut, the delay is removed. To explain further, some alarms have, incorporated in the signalling set up, a delay, which means that when the alarm is activated there is, say, a 10 minute delay before the bells start to ring, but in the meantime the remote signalling has been activated. Now it is obvious that the cutting of the telephone line removes the remote signalling, so the delay in the bell ringing is no longer apposite, and is removed by this additional equipment. The logic behind the delay in bell ringing is to give the police a chance of arriving at the premises and making an arrest before the bells scare off the intruder.

(ii) when the line is cut between the protected premises and the first telephone exchange on its route to the central station, the bells start to ring at that very moment, ie, not awaiting a subsequent break-in to the premises.

You are probably asking why I have not identified each piece of equipment with the relevant action. Well there is a simple reason. They are differently referred to by different people, and were I to make a definitive statement as to which is which, it could result in you making an error depending upon to whom you are talking.

Regrettably, alarm specifications can once again be very misleading, but I would not go as far as to say that it was intentional. I have experienced (i) above being described in terms which made the reader feel that the cutting of the line resulted in *'instant bells'*. It does, but what does *'instant bells'* mean. Does it mean that at the moment the line is cut the bells ring, or does it mean that there will be instant bells when there is an intrusion, ie no delay?. Subtle difference. I have telephoned an alarm company to query this type of description and been met with the *'oh, I don't know'* reply. I can only suggest that if the position is not clear you must assume the worst.

Whatever the meaning of the additional equipment, the point which is still of greatest importance is that no signal will be transmitted to anyone, nor will anyone know at the distant end. At the customer's end there should be an audible signal, which gives the client time to do something if he is still there, but does nothing if the premises are vacated.

Whereas 999's send a speech message to the emergency telephone operator, Digital Communicators send an electrically pulsed, coded, digital message to a central station. The message is sent by a transmitter/receiver at the protected premises to a similar piece of equipment at the central station. The messages are completely unintelligible to the human ear but quite understandable to matched pieces of equipment.

The transmitter at the protected premises, electronically, at high speed, dials the telephone number which has been programmed into it, usually that of a central station. When contact is established, this is usually acknowledged by the receiver at the central station. If this acknowledgement is not received, the transmitter closes down and tries again, and can do so for up to 5 times until it makes a good connection. It is readily seen that this is a great improvement on the 999 which only has one attempt at dialling and will transmit its message to anyone whether it is the correct person or not. The digital communicator has, therefore, a very limited ability to think. Having established contact with the central station, the transmitter transmits its message, and the receiver has to receive two consecutive correct messages before it assumes that the message has been received. When this is done, the transmitter at the central station then sends an acknowledgement message, known as the handshake, back to the protected premises, which is a signal to the transmitter at the protected premises to close down. This sounds as if it must take a very long time to achieve, but because everything is done in electronic codes, each section takes milliseconds and the whole process is very quick indeed.

As with 999 units, the telephone line should be *'outgoing calls only'* to prevent attempts to engage the line before an attack is made.

I said that the signal sent is very quick, and it is, but it is not at the speed of light, so there is still need to be careful as to the siting of the transmission unit to prevent attack before the signal is completely transmitted.

Another advantage of the digital communicator over the 999 is its ability to send more than one form of message, depending upon what triggered the signalling equipment. Most units can cope with up to 8 differing messages, such as Fire, Theft, Personal Attack, Refrigeration, Boiler etc, the two most common being Theft and Personal Attack. This can be very important as far as we are concerned. If the central station receives a personal attack signal, it should, and most probably will, be sent to the Police in that form, so that they are likely to give it more attention than an ordinary theft, as there is likely to be danger to human life involved. I wonder how often this facility is used and, more important, how often it is defined in the specification?

Whereas a 999 unit dials exactly that, 999, and gets the local police headquarters (via the Telephone Exchange) a digital communicator can be programmed to dial any number in Britain, the actual number concerned being programmed into the unit at the time of installation, although it can be easily amended at a later date if required. This facility has both advantages and disadvantages (now isn't that surprising?). In remote areas, eg the mountains of Wales, it is possible to have a central station connection although the actual central station may be quite a distance away, and the cost involved is still reasonable. The disadvantage is that if you are not careful you may be accepting a connection to a central station in an area which is not where you think it is, and in an area which you did not appreciate. Several years ago, a London Installer used to have its equipment dial a number in Glasgow, and even now there is an installer operating in London which has its equipment dial to the Midlands unless you ask for something different. The two major snags with this type of situation are (a) there is virtually no likelihood of the central station involved having a direct speech line to the Police Authority where the risk is located. This in turn means that the central station must use the normal network service to make contact with the relevant Police Force and, if the distance is sufficiently great, then they have all of the potential chances of misrouting, engaged lines from one exchange to another etc, etc. (b) the further the call has to go from the protected premises to the central station, the more chance it has of being similarly misrouted etc. All of these snags cause delay in letting the Police even have a chance of being efficient. There are, of course, instances where this lengthy route is unavoidable, but where it can be avoided it should be. For security reasons, most Alarm Companies do not specify the exact location of the central station they are utilising on their specifications, so if you have any doubts you have little alternative but to enquire.

I am in no doubt of the benefits of the digital communicator system, but at the same time I am in no doubt about its limitations.

Direct Line Signalling (sometimes called Central Station Line) There is a lot of misleading talk in general terms about this type of signalling, some of which could even be intentional. I am not referring to the technicalities of the system, but once again to what is actually being referred to when the term is mentioned. In the days before digital communicator's were about, Central Station Lines or connections was another way of referring to Direct Lines. However, now that we do have digital communicator's which also go to a central station it is wrong to talk about a *Central Station Connection'* without amplifying what is meant. At least one installer I know of, on the subject of remote signalling, heads its paragraph in bold print *'Central Station Connection'*, and then in smaller print goes on to talk about a digital communicator, and I know that it causes confusion.

We could get very technical here, but I won't, only general principles will be discussed. I will put the reason down as a desire not to confuse.

Digital communicator's, 999's etc all use normal speech lines for the transmission of the alarm signals, ie the lines we use for everyday calls. Direct Line equipment does not. The line connection between the protected premises and the central station is used for alarm purposes only and it is a permanent connection which cannot misroute, become engaged etc. The quality of the line is superior (and even then there are different grades available) to that normally used, and special connection arrangements are made within the exchanges.

Because of all this let there be no doubt in your mind that the costs involved with this form of signalling are very much higher, both at installation time and on an annual line rental basis, than all of the other forms of remote signalling mentioned. When this form of signalling was first introduced, and in some cases these still exist, there was only one alarm on each line into the central station, so all of the costs had to be borne by the subscriber involved. At today's prices such costs are horrendous. Consequently they are not used very often. That is not to say that you cannot use such a system if you think that the case warrants it, eg a Bullion Store or the like. To reduce costs to a more acceptable level, (brought about by vast annual increases in line charges) methods have been developed whereby each line is shared by several subscribers. A *'bearer line'* is laid from the central station to an area where the Alarm Company thinks that it will get a fair amount of business. Several subscribers are then latched on to that line at various points along its route and each subscriber only has to pay for a proportion of the bearer line plus his connection on to it, a great saving on the original method.

The signals (messages) sent down these lines are all electronic, not speech, and (virtually) impossible to reproduce (by a would be burglar), because they are random, pulsed, speedy and other technical terms which in total mean complicated. These signals can go in both directions, ie, to and from the protected premises and the central station. As a result, the central station can monitor both the line to see that it has not been cut (otherwise the signals would not get through), and the state of the alarm system at any connected premises. To all intents and purposes the central station asks the system "how are you" and gets the reply *"ok"*, or *'I am in an alarm condition"*. Depending upon the reply, the central station either says nothing or acts by advising the appropriate authority. This form of two way transmission is often referred to as "return path signalling". Older equipment, and cheaper versions used today, probably did not have this capability, signals only going from the protected premises to the Central Station. There was, therefore, no interrogation being carried out on the condition of the alarm, and it would not be until it tried to operate that any fault or defect other than a line fault would be apparent. Regrettably, once again it is extremely doubtful whether this information will be contained in any specification.

The transmitters in the protected premises and the central station are quite sophisticated, but most importantly they are matched at the time of installation, so that although the equipment at the protected premises can *'talk'* to the central station it cannot talk to any equipment at other protected premises. However, the equipment at the central station can talk to many protected premises individually, more than is on any one line. This might initially make you think that the interrogation of each system must be at lengthy intervals, but not so. The speed of the signals is measured in milliseconds so the system is quick. Also, any good central station does not overload any of its equipment before having additional units installed.

I said earlier that the signalling could detect when the line is cut. If this happens when the system is *'on'*, then it should be treated as an alarm, but if the system is *'off'*, the subscriber should be made aware of the situation so that the appropriate action can be taken.

Most Direct Line systems work on the same principle; they all have subtle differences and are called fancy names, but unless you are aware of the deficiencies of any particular system then I suggest that you treat them all alike. However, remember that at the moment we are talking about Direct Line signalling to central stations and NOT the central station's themselves, or for that matter the Alarm Companies.

To all intents and purposes the signal is instant so, if the transmission unit were to be attacked, it would show up in the central station either as an alarm or a line fault, but in either case should be actioned. This does not mean, however, that you can site the transmitter unit anywhere as to do so would show signs of carelessness in that you would be encouraging attack, and the cost of the equipment is not inconsiderable.

Although line costs make it unlikely that these systems will cover vast distances between the protected premises and the central station, it is still possible that the central station will not be in the same geographical area as the risk, as far as Police response is concerned. You could, therefore, face the same problem over speech between the central station and the Police as mentioned earlier under digital communicators, but because of the shorter distances the problem should not be as severe.

Red Care is a signalling system developed by British Telecom, available in certain parts of the country only, but it is spreading. Where it fits in to the scale of security signalling is still being debated in some quarters and I suggest that you consult your employers to establish how they regard it.

The signalling uses, as far as the client is concerned, his normal telephone line, thus there is no requirement for a separate or special line, the cost saving usually being appreciated by the client. The signalling is transmitted by a transmitter in the protected premises to equipment in British Telecom premises. These premises are said to be secure etc but, as far as I am aware, there has been no independent examination of them, so we are left with British Telecom's assertion upon which we have to rely. That comment is not intended to infer that the security of the premises concerned is poor — I would however be happier with either (a) some greater detail, or (b) independent inspection and concurrence with the statement. Without going into technicalities, the signal is processed, analysed etc by computers and, depending upon the result, it is either simply acknowledged or acted upon by passing further information on to the relevant authority. That could be the Fire Brigade, a Central Station, an engineer of the client or whoever has the appropriate equipment to receive the relevant message. It is then up to that person or Company or Brigade to take any necessary further action. The signal has by that time done its work and it is now up to others to complete the process.

As with all modern signalling developments, the actual signal is a series of bleeps, blips and similar, all quite unintelligible to the human, but quite coherent to a matched computer. Another, very important, point about this signal is that it is above the range of the average ear and therefore can be constantly transmitted down the line even when the client is using his telephone. He won't hear it. This does in fact happen, ie the line and alarm state is constantly being monitored. Cutting the line is known to British Telecom, and engaging the line is ineffective as the signal continues to transmit regardless.

No significance should be placed upon the positioning I have given to the detailing of signalling systems. The order up to Red Care is generally accepted, but Red Care must be slotted in somewhere depending upon your employer's thoughts on the matter.

Although this is new, I, personally, feel that it will spread and that you will meet it (or its children) as your career progresses.

Central Stations

Unfortunately this term has been used for many years and has come to be accepted as a general term for a *'receiving station for Intruder Alarm transmissions, other than Police premises "*, (that is my definition). Now if you think of that, it could mean virtually anything you want it to. The spare bedroom, the garden shed, the garage, the most sophisticated purpose built building, etc, etc. So, in any particular case, what are you involved with?.

Regretfully the Insurance Industry doesn't seem to care, at least that is the impression one is inclined to get. There has been no overall approach to *'grade or approve'* those in use.

Any time I bring up this subject, I usually get a response along the lines of *'so what, none have been attacked, and you couldn't prove inefficiency even if it happened"*.

So for all practical purposes, I could just repeat the first paragraph and leave it at that. However, being the stubborn, pig-headed swine that I am, I will continue. There is a great variety of central stations, both in equipment and efficiency, but at least they all appear to be trying to do roughly the same thing. The purpose is to receive and send messages ('signals) to alarm installations, interrogate and analyse the responses received, and act accordingly by calling the Subscriber, Police, Fire etc. depending upon the signal analysis. This must be done swiftly, correctly and efficiently.

Not very long ago, a British Standard was devised for Central Stations, covering construction and operating/manning procedures. Companies were given 5 years to implement it, otherwise they could not say that their central station was to British Standard. This Standard has hit many snags, and to be honest I can't see it having much impact unless it is changed. Amongst the snags are:—

(1) There are too many *'shoulds'* and *'coulds'* where the word needed was *'must'*, so those concerned have been given ready made *'let outs'* for using alternatives.

(2) The cost of updating many central stations which have been hitherto considered as amongst those acceptable, is, in many cases, quite enormous, especially when you consider that it includes *'collector stations'* as used by certain companies.

(3) Every premises used in this connection is liable to inspection at a fairly hefty fee, so the more you have the more the annual inspection costs.

(4) The Standard DOES NOT apply to premises which terminate digital communicators **only**.

If you are not careful you might be accepting as a central station termination point, *'Granny's Attic'*.

Monitored opening and closing — This must be explained as it is a facility which is often used and more often misused.

The concept is that most businesses have set hours of operation which do not vary very much or very often. It follows that the premises should only be open during these hours and that in that period only should the alarm be in the *'off'* position. There have been occasions where keyholders have been forced to permit entry to criminals due to threats of violence. Because the keyholder is the person involuntarily involved, the keys will be used to turn off the alarm should it already have been set. If the alarm had not yet been set then it would not be done at the usual time. Let us assume that after the intrusion was complete the intruder (or his *'prisoner'*) set the alarm, nothing would normally be seen as untoward at the Central Station. The same events in essence could occur at any time during the normally closed period as long as keys were used; and nothing would be suspected. If, however, the signalling is *'monitored'* for opening and closing, this type of event would be treated as an alarm and actioned accordingly.

How then does the monitoring operate?. The client and the alarm company agree on the times when the alarm should be in the *'set'* condition. Any opening or closing outside these periods will be treated as an alarm. That sounds simple doesn't it?. Well it is not as simple as it seems. For a start, allowance must be made for lateness due to short periods of activity after the normal period of closing, for example if a client is in the middle of a very important telephone conversation when closing time arrives. It is not really good business to tell his customer that he must go as it is time to set the alarm. At opening it is not acceptable to expect the client to wait outside his premise for a minute as he is too early to go in. It follows, therefore, that some *'latitude'* must be inbuilt to the agreed times of business. If we assume that a business is normally open from 8 am to 6 pm, it would appear to be reasonable to have the agreed times as 7.55 am to 6.10 pm. There are going to be occasions where even that latitude is not going to be sufficient, but they should not be often (if they are often, then the agreed times are wrong), and this is catered for by the client being issued with a password by the Central Station, and the use of this password can gain temporary dispensation of the agreed times and another time will be agreed at the time of change. However, I must emphasise that this will only be agreed for a temporary and short period. If the change is to last for days or weeks, then the agreement should be confirmed in writing. The password must be used carefully. It is no use going into the premises 10 minutes before you should have and then phoning the central station to use the password, nor is it any use to phone after the agreed closing time has past. Agreement must be made before entry and before the closing time has expired. Failure to do so could be the result of duress being used and would therefore defeat the whole purpose of the exercise.

What happens if the alarm is set or unset outside the agreed hours?. Well I suppose that you would expect the alarm to be actioned immediately by the Central Station. Guess what, it is not quite that simple. For a start the procedures adopted by different Central Stations are not all the same. I get the impression that the actions taken are fairly standard if the premises are

107

opened either (i) slightly early, or (ii) at a time well outside the recognised hours of opening. The alarm would be actioned immediately. However, if the client does not lock up on time there can be quite a process before the police are summoned. Some Central Station operators try to contact the Keyholder either at the premises or at his home to see if there has been an error made or what the situation is. Now, this can obviously take some time and it might not be agreeable to your employer that such time should be used in that way. You might want immediate action. As I said, the actions of differing Central Stations vary, so do you know what is going to happen anyway?.

Now all of the above is about a good facility, but only if it is used properly. The snag is that the majority of usage is (a) not thought out properly, or (b) not necessary in the first place. Think carefully, does your client really warrant the use of this facility? I said earlier that the reason for the development was the occasions where duress was used on the keyholder. There is no doubt that this does occur, but it does not happen all that often and usually only where the risk is particularly large or high amounts of cash are involved.

There is a tremendous similarity between the majority of times that businesses open and close. If they all were to use this facility what would be the result?. (i) telephone lines would be completely jammed (remember that digital communicators use the normal switched network) (ii) a great bulge in the work process at the Central Station necessitating extra staff to cope (or alternatively a backlog building up), and (iii) a great *'peak'* in the number of false alarms occurring with incorrect alarm setting. This latter point is not a theory of mine, it is a fact which can be verified by Police Authority records. There is little doubt that incorrect alarm setting and digressing from agreed times cause the Police a tremendous headache.

Let us just ponder for a while on the problems this causes the Police. These peaks of activity, the vast majority being false alarms, cause (i) apathy and scepticism to grow in their respect for alarms, (ii) They are expected to fly around like bluebottles (or something similar) at times when traffic is at its worst like peak hour jams, and (iii) they must inevitably *'miss'* the genuine calls because they are chasing the false calls.

Think also of the constraints which the facility places upon your client. Assume that he arrives early, say 10 minutes, and it is pouring cats and dogs. He can't go in without first finding a 'phone to pass over the password. He might buy his wife a present and leave it in his desk, then he suddenly remembers when he is in his car. He can't just go back in and collect it, he must first 'phone the Central Station.

Now don't go away with the idea that I want this facility withdrawn, far from it, but I do want to see it used properly and not with gay (oops, sorry — free) abandon, as I feel is the case now.

CHAPTER 15
C.C.T.V. & Guarding

Once again I would remind all readers that this book is designed and intended for novice surveyors, and other people of similar experience who become involved in security design or in understanding security requirements. For that reason I have no intention of going into CCTV or guarding facilities in other than very basic terms. To be more detailed and technical would, I think, cause confusion and I do not think many surveyors of the novice standard are likely, in practice, to get involved. Such cases as deserve these services would, quite correctly, be taken over by someone of greater experience. However, I feel it advantageous to the junior surveyor to have a knowledge of the basic concepts so that, if these services would be beneficial, they can be considered and discussed with more senior surveyors.

To a certain extent manned guarding and CCTV are doing the same thing and the latter could be considered as being the more mechanised modern method of the former.

Manned guarding does not prevent all losses at the specified premises although, hopefully, it does reduce them considerably. The presence of a person on the premises must be a deterrent to many would-be burglars. This must, however, be a theoretical, logical argument as, if a burglar does not attack, unless he admits to thinking of it later, no-one knows he has not attacked. As many of you will have read in the press over the years there are burglars who will not be deterred by the presence of another human being and, regrettably, will use violence to overcome the guards.

If you have a risk where manned guards are to be employed there are many things that must be considered before embarking on such a venture.

For a start, do not be confused by static guards on the premises and guards who visit the premises at intervals throughout specified periods. Unfortunately, lax wording of letters can cause this very confusion, and if you receive the message at second, third or even fourth hand it is more likely that the exact form of guarding offered will have become vague to put it midly. Unbelievable as it may seem to you, some clients do not even know there is a difference between the two forms of guarding.

Guards who's job is to visit at regular intervals invariably have a fairly set route of premises to be visited and if this *'route'* is followed without any variation the result is a virtual timetable, i.e. if it takes $1\frac{1}{2}$ hours to visit all the premises on the schedule it will probably result in your client being visited at $1\frac{1}{2}$ hour intervals. It does not take a burglar of high intelligence to work out the advantages of $1\frac{1}{2}$ hours to work away on premises with the probability of no interruption. As these guards usually use clearly distinguished vehicles it makes the job of a *'look-out'* quite simple. Whilst this form of *'guarding'* may have its place in the security field I feel it is very limited. In all probability the main advantage likely to be derived is that of discovering that an intrusion has already taken place and that the *'bird has long since flown'*. This may be a definite objective but can hardly be called preventive.

Guards who are permanently on the premises, known as *'static guards'*, are a different matter altogether, but even with them you must be careful. The good ones are very good and the bad ones are rubbish, and you have all of the gradings in between. Starting at the bottom end of the range you will find the client who maintains he has his *'own guard'* in whom he has complete faith. In many cases that terminology is the same as saying *'an old established employee who is now too old and unfit to work and now sleeps on the premises with his pet poodle';* hardly an adversary likely to put the fear of death into some of the hardened *'no holds barred'* burglars which bedevil our society today. A night watchman and a security guard are not the same regardless of the client's assertions.

Even within the various professional guarding companies there is a range of standards. Although the British Security Industry Association (BSIA) has standards, inspections and the like, there is absolutely no compulsion on any guarding company to be a member of the BSIA, and there are no legal regulations, or even guidelines, for the establishment of a guarding company despite the seriousness of the type of business in which they are involved. It is, therefore, up to the client and yourself to be satisfied that the guarding company involved is acceptable. I would suggest that if it is the first time you, or any of your fellow surveyors, have encountered the company you should enquire, and satisfy yourself, about recruiting methods, screening of applicants, references, training, turnover of staff (a rapid turnover could indicate something basically wrong with the management), supervision, etc. You should also enquire about how the system, or organisation, of the contract with which you are involved has been devised e.g. how often do the guards have to check with Central Control?, what happens if the guard fails to do so?, are secret passwords used (essential in case the guard is under duress at the time he makes the check call)?, what back-up is there if a guard falls ill during his tour of duty? These are points which apply to all contracts regardless of size or degree of complexity, and no doubt you may think of other relevant points. I have no intention of trying to compile a complete list of points to be raised as it is not my intention to lay down your's or your employer's methods of working but, hopefully, the foregoing will have given you an indication of the depth of questioning required. I am always suspicious of any company which refuses to answer reasonable questions properly and politely asked; does their refusal to answer infer something to hide? As many surveyor's employer's own security is notoriously abysmal I can understand reluctance to answer some points in writing, but a personal visit should overcome these problems.

Having satisfied yourself as to the Guarding Company involved you should also examine the detail of the contract between the Guarding Company and your client. If you do not do so you may well find later, usually after a loss has been sustained, that the guarding was not as comprehensive as you thought it was or would have insisted upon before being satisfied. Amongst the points you should consider are (a) the area to be patrolled or observed; in a large building or complex you may only be worried about some of the areas involved, (b) can the area of concern be observed from one point without the need for patrol? (c) if patrolling is required are there sufficient check points to ensure the patrol is being properly carried out? (d) is the patrol area so large that the time gap between checks is sufficient for a break-in to occur? (e) is the patrolling guard in radio contact with anyone, if so where is that *'other person'*? (f) does the patrolling interfere in any way with an intruder alarm upon which you also rely? Having assessed all of these factors and the others which you consider relevant you must then decide how many guards you feel are required to provide the security you consider to be adequate. Remember, you are talking about guards who are human so don't expect them to walk on patrol non-stop for 8 hours or whatever length the shift may be. Guards can be quite costly, it must be at least £10,000 per man per annum, and you will require more men at weekends and over holiday periods than during weekday evenings and nights. When you add up the cost you will probably be quite surprised unless you have gone through this process before. Don't misunderstand me, I am in no way saying that guarding services are too expensive to be appropriate. There are definite circumstances where they are the perfect, maybe the only, answer. However, the cost makes it even more essential that you make sure you and your client are dealing with a good, well organised, company, otherwise the *'cowboy'* you employ is going to be a very costly mistake.

Near the beginning of this chapter I inferred that Security Guards and CCTV were virtually doing the same thing. A guard is, or at least should be, aware of the situation and conditions of property he is guarding and if anything significant changes he should act accordingly. A CCTV camera is also looking at a particular set of circumstances and, if something changes, action should be taken. There is of course a great variety of ways the system can be arranged and it depends upon the arrangement as to what action ensues. You can have a single camera looking at a specific object, e.g. a safe, transmitting a signal to a monitor at another part of the same building or even in another building altogether. The means by which the camera and screen are connected to each other depends on distance and other factors too technical for this book.

If necessary there can be several such cameras looking at individual objects, all connected to the same monitor screen, the screen operator being able to select which is viewed or, alternatively, they can appear in sequence. These cameras can also be *'programmed'* so that a change in the picture the camera transmits automatically means that that picture *'jumps the queue'* and appears on the operator's screen.

Cameras can be rigidly fixed or can be constantly scanning an area. The operator can override the automatic scan if he sees something of interest and can, if required, *'zoom'* in for a closer look.

Systems can be devised to video record constantly, by command of the VDU operator or by automatic initiation when there is a *'change of state'* being viewed by the camera. These video recordings can be dated and timed automatically in case they are later required as evidence in some investigation. Cameras can be used externally as well as internally and can be used during business hours as well as when the premises are *'quiet'.*

Assuming the VDU operator is adequately trained the system can be used to monitor automatic manufacturing processes, flow systems, refrigeration temperatures or the like. This can be a *'sales point'* if you are having difficulty *'selling'* the idea to your client.

You will see from the above that the variety of tasks the equipment can perform is quite considerable and from an observation point of view you can virtually say that anything a human sees can also be seen by a camera. However, a guard cannot be in several places at one time whereas all of the cameras can be operational simultaneously. You can have individual viewing screens per camera and one operator can probably supervise up to 10 screens. If the screens cater for more than one camera each, an individual operator can view in comfort and safety rather than be exposed to weather and potential danger. Unless the system requires extension or amendment you only purchase the equipment once, but it must be fully and adequately maintained, whereas guards have to be paid for every year.

However, before you go overboard on the idea of CCTV I must point out that it is much more complicated than I have suggested so far, and expert knowledge of lighting, equipment and environment is an absolute essential as any one of these factors wrongly evaluated can ruin the whole concept! It is almost inevitable in complex cases that a variety and combination of cameras will be necessary and they all have their proper place in a system. Just as with alarms, guards, locks and every other form of security there is good equipment and bad equipment, good companies and bad companies — be careful.

Unless you are an expert in this field I strongly recommend you obtain the guidance and advice of a specialist. The purchase price can be quite considerable, but it is basically a *'one off'* payment (plus the maintenance of course), which must not be wasted.

There can be cases where a combination of guarding and CCTV is the answer. You must be prepared to adapt and compromise to find the best solution for your particular case. No-one, certainly not I, can tell you in advance what your risk requires.

CHAPTER 16
Safes

Previously we have considered protection of goods etc. either by alarming the location or by strengthening the structure housing these goods. We will now consider purpose made housings for valuables, i.e. safes.

What is a safe? Well there's a good question to start with. I should imagine ten dictionaries would give ten different definitions. However, I think we must assume that the normal conception of a safe as a strong metal box for keeping valuables secure, is accepted. As a matter of interest, how many Insurers with safe warranties or conditions in their policies define what they consider to be a safe?

Safes have been with us for many many years so, naturally, as with virtually every other manufactured item, there have been vast changes and improvements. Safemaking has always been a highly respected profession (although they have their *'cowboys'* just like every other trade), consequently some very old safes have very imposing appearances to the non professional eye, and owners are often under the false impression that they have a much superior piece of equipment to that which they actually possess. Strength presents different impressions to different observers. I, like most other experienced surveyors, have encountered many safes which I can understand fool the owners and I sympathise with them. What probably adds to the illusion is that older safes tend to be more ornate and have equally ornate nameplates with misleading descriptions. These are misleading in light of today's knowledge, but were probably not at the time of manufacture.

Safes fall into three broad types, i.e. free standing, wall and underfloor.

Free standing safes are basically *'box shaped'* with a single leaf door, although some older models did have double leaf doors. The earliest type, commonly found today despite their age, is the square bodied safe where sides, top, bottom are separate plates of metal joined to each other at right angles, being screwed or rivetted onto an angle iron frame. These safes are able to be virtually dismantled by crude implements. This type of safe is illustrated in figure 75 overleaf.

Because the square edged (cornered) safe could be taken to pieces fairly easily, manufacturers progressed by adding metal bands around the safe in an attempt to *'hold it together'*, hence the *'banded safe'*, see figure 76 overleaf. This may have helped to keep the safe in one piece, but did nothing to improve the strength of the actual materials involved, so the improvement is not really significant.

Because one of the favourite points of attack was the right angle junctions of the sheets of metal, the next development was to remove some of these junctions. This was achieved by the top, sides and bottom being one piece of metal, bent round, and jointed at the centre of the bottom of the safe where it is inaccessible. The end product is called a *'Four corner bent'* safe, see figure 77. This, however, still left the back of the safe affixed to the remainder of the body as in the square body construction.

To improve this situation the safe was *'banded'*, just as the square edged safe had been banded before. However, the rearmost bands were set further back than the body of the safe and bent over to overlap the joint with the body. The back plate was pushed in from the front until it met the bent over band.

The next development was for the body itself to be bent over at the back of the safe, instead of using the reinforcing bands. So the sides, top and bottom are much greater in size than necessary, the excess being bent over to retain the back plate which was still separate and inserted from the front. This safe is known as the *'eight corner bent'* safe.

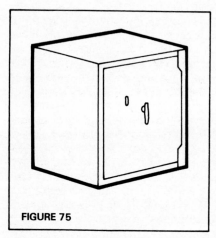

FIGURE 75

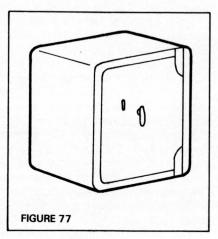

FIGURE 77

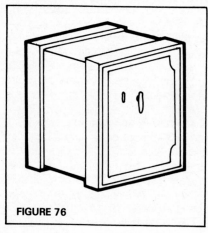

FIGURE 76

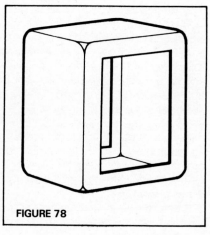

FIGURE 78

The next stage in development was fairly logical and that was to bend the sides, top and bottom of the safe at the front as well as at the back. This, of course, required an internal framework for back plate and door frame fixings to be inserted prior to the main body bending operation taking place. This safe is known as the *twelve corner bent* safe, and is illustrated in figure 78.

Up until this stage of progression it appears that the prime objective of improvements was to prevent the removal of complete sections of the safe body by improving the means by which they were held to each other. In addition to the changing shape as previously described, over a period welding superceded screws or rivets, so that the actual junctions are harder to physically prise apart. If you think about what has been already written you will realise that, as the back is *inserted against the rear flanges from the front* it is not possible for the flanges and the back plate to be flush with each other. This is often *disguised* by an additional plate being affixed to the back plate, externally, to produce a flush finish. Bear this in mind, and do not confuse such a safe with the modern safes mentioned shortly.

Nothing, so far, has been mentioned of methods to improve the actual strength of the safe materials. The sheets of metal used can range from very thin to $\frac{1}{2}$" thickness, but in a well produced and maintained safe you may have difficulty in finding out just how thick those plates are. The thinner varieties can be opened by the proverbial *tin opener*, so all the flanges, bands, welding etc. achieve very little if the burglar has much between his ears and even fairly basic equipment.

To counter attacks by drilling and oxyacetylene cutting, lining materials were added. However, there are cases where these linings are not laminated together or properly and securely fixed to the outer shell, so that separation can take place under attack. In order to add weight, and in some instances to increase fire resistance, materials were added between the layers of metal but the quality of these *infills* varied tremendously and, in some cases, with age, the material deteriorated so much as to end up as powder near the foot of the safe, leaving hollows further up the sides.

This *infill* was eventually superseded by concrete which remained more stable, but basically you still had a safe of *bits and pieces* bolted, rivetted or welded together.

Modern safes have the inner body cast in one piece with no seams, joints, etc. This inner body is faced with the materials which are designed to counter the varying forms of attack and then inserted in an outer shell, which is also cast in one piece, which, although strong in itself, has as its prime objective *keeping the rest of the equipment together*.

There are two principal reasons for not going into detail regarding the modern component materials. The first is basically for security reasons; if I broadcast them here, it may give some people the wrong idea. The second is that manufacturers have their own variations and it is, therefore, impossible to generalise. However, I feel it is true to say that most of the better known British made safes are well equipped to stand up to the majority of modern attacks. That may, to some people, appear to be a rash statement to make, but I will endeavour to justify it later when talking about siting etc.

Just as there was gradual development in the construction of safe bodies, there was a corresponding development in safe doors. It is self evident that, as near as is humanly possible, the strength of the two sections, i.e. body and door, must be equal; to do otherwise is a waste of time and money.

In the early days the door was a steel plate with the lock case i.e. the lock and boltwork literally bolted onto the back. Severe blows could, on occasions, cause the boltwork to 'fall off'.

To improve matters the boltwork moved in brackets, through holes cut in angle iron reinforcement which was fitted all round the door edge. Strengthening plates were sometimes, but by no means always, added.

The modern safe door barely resembles its predecessors. A strong metal box is constructed and welded onto the back of the safe door, which itself should have the same resistance features as the safe body. This metal box contains the locking mechanism which, in a good safe should be quite complex and sophisticated. The lockcase should house, in addition to the normal locking mechanism, automatic relocking devices designed to act if the safe door is attacked. This means that if the normal locking devices become so weakened or otherwise compromised that they can not be moved by the door handle, these relocking devices 'over-ride' and prevent opening. Once again, for security reasons, I do not intend to go further into these devices, but would suggest that any reader wishing to gain more information can, if they present themselves properly, be acquainted of individual manufacturer's methods by approaching the manufacturers direct. I would suggest this is best organised by your employer as groups (small) would probably be more appreciated by the manufacturers than a constant stream of individuals.

The number of bolts holding a safe door closed depends upon two things, i.e. the size of the door and the quality of safe involved. However, do not be fooled into thinking that many bolts *must* mean a good safe; it could be a means to mislead the observer. The handle on the face of the door, when rotated, will either lock or unlock, i.e. move the bolts outwards or retract them. There will always be movable bolts on the locking edge of the door, but a good safe door will also have them on the top and bottom edge. Every door should have either (a) moving bolts or (b) fixed hinge bolts (sometimes one continuous fixed bolt) on the hinge edge of the door. Failure to do so does, in my opinion, severely lower the grade of the safe. The hinges on a safe door are primarily to facilitate opening and closing and, whilst they look strong, and in many cases are, the fact that they nearly always protrude makes them vulnerable to attack, hence the necessity for hinge bolts, fixed or moving. You will see, therefore, that the door is 'locked in' on all four edges making illegal opening much more difficult than if the bolts were only on one edge.

The subject of method of locking, i.e. key, combination or other, will be discussed later.

Wall safes are virtually metal boxes which are set into the relevant wall. It is customary to refer to those safes in terms relative to brick sizes, e.g. single brick, two brick etc., this indicating a safe the size of two bricks, one on top of the other. Where greater depth than one brick is required, brick reference is still used but be careful, a safe 2 bricks high and 2 bricks deep is a '4 brick cube' safe. Some manufacturers vary this practice but the above is generally true.

116

The safe itself is just a box of welded metal up to ¼" thick. The doors are similar or thicker, seldom thinner, but they rebate into slots made in the safe body, or behind protective plates welded onto the safe, thus removing fears of the hinge being a particular weakness. The securing of the door is by a bolt or bolts fitting into recesses in the safe body, or behind welded protective securing plates. These bolts are moved either by the lock key movement, or by a handle on the face of the door which, when turned, moves the bolts.

There are obvious (or at least they should be obvious) problems regarding wall safe siting. By the very nature of a wall safe it is necessary to remove part of the wall to insert the safe. Therefore, a single brick safe in a single brick thick (4½") wall or a 4 brick cube safe in a double brick thick wall (9" with no cavity) must have the rear of the safe exposed on the reverse side of the wall concerned. Even with a double brick cavity wall, the amount of brick preventing rear exposure is only the thickness of the cavity, and it is almost inevitable that the brick remaining has been weakened by the physical activities involved in removing part of the brickwork. The foregoing illustrates the difficulty in finding an appropriate wall for siting a safe of this nature. I have frequently found safes poorly sited, where the rear of the safe is easily accessible, and if sufficient pressure were applied the safe could be *'pushed out'*.

Some safes have added *'equipment'* to prevent the foregoing type of removal, but they are only effective if very expertly installed. As all of these preventive devices, plates, bolts and the like, are concealed once the safe has been installed, the surveyor has no way of knowing (a) whether or not they are actually present, and (b) whether the method of installation has been sufficiently professional to make these devices effective.

Where is the best place to site a wall safe, presuming of course that the wall is adequate? I doubt very much if there is such a thing as a practical place where *'the burglar will never think of looking'*. They have all been used before and burglars who are prepared to attack safes are not *'young yobos'*; they have a certain amount of intelligence, so they won't be fooled easily. If you think of a place which is so obscure as to fool the burglar, the chances are that this place will be so inconvenient that the client will not use the safe properly. Because of the sizes of these safes their most likely use is for keeping small items such as jewellery. Now the lady of the house returning from a dinner, ball, theatre or some other such occasion, is hardly likely to clamber under the bed, into the loft, down to the cellar or below the kitchen sink to replace the jewellery. The dressing table *'will do for the night'*, then it's forgotten.

Under floor safes, would you believe, are intended to be sited under floors. The safe itself is made of metal, welded at its junctions, the metal thickness varying depending upon the manufacturers concerned. A slight variation in shape is developing, but the majority are cylinders or boxes.

These safes can be installed with the safe door virtually flush with the floor, but this is to be discouraged as it leaves the door too accessible for physical attack by simple means. Far better are those which have been made with, or fitted with at the time of installation, a funnel or neck which is virtually a cylinder, usually about 6" in length and with a diameter slightly larger than that of the door itself. This neck means that the door of the safe is now about

6" below the floor surface, and less accessible for attack. This neck does have two bad effects, but they do not equate to the advantage, they being (a) it means that the safe user has even further to reach down to retrieve the safe contents, and (b) dust can accumulate over the safe door (and keyhole) if the safe is not used often. This latter problem is easily overcome, but often missed, by the use of a plastic *'lid'* or dustcover, flush with the floor.

These necks can, of course, be rectangular for rectangular shaped safes, but the same considerations and principles apply.

Some safes have separate deposit *'traps'* which allow *'goods'*, usually money in canisters, to be deposited when the safe is locked, a good facility for shops etc., where the keys can be held by someone in authority but the staff can still remove the cash from more vulnerable places. This chute should be too thin for anyone to insert an arm to remove the contents, and at the foot of the chute, in the safe chamber, there should be baffle plates which deflect the deposited contents away from the chute bottom and prevent anyone *'fishing'* the contents back out. One point to be borne in mind is that the safe chamber should be large enough to hold all the deposit canisters without them stacking back and blocking the deposit chute, a problem which could arise, for example, with extremely busy filling stations. The funnel and deposit chute length varies with the manufacturer and with the location. If need be these can be lengthened, but this usually causes problems when trying to empty the safe. An illustration of a deposit floor safe is given in figure 79.

The doors for these safes can vary quite considerably, but because they are intended to be set into strong floors there is no major weight problem (other than being able to be lifted by the keyholder), so they can be quite thick and strong. The doors, which are in many cases completely detachable and removeable, must be held by moving lock bolts which come out of the lid at varying points around it. To be effective there must be at least three such bolts. Some doors, especially in rectangular funnels, are hinged, but, personally, I am not too keen on these, as I can easily imagine

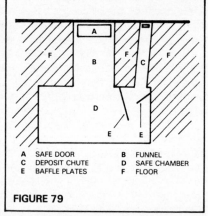

A	SAFE DOOR	B	FUNNEL
C	DEPOSIT CHUTE	D	SAFE CHAMBER
E	BAFFLE PLATES	F	FLOOR

FIGURE 79

someone with their arm down in the safe chamber and the lid dropping on their arm injuring them. To counter this the door would have to be spring loaded and I fear many are not. You should be aware of this, as you may be specifying something which could cause injury to your customer or his employee.

The majority of locking methods are on two bases, i.e. keylock, or combination lock (or both). The usual question asked is *'which is the better of the two'?* Unfortunately, like so many other problems in security, I do not think there is a straightforward answer; it depends upon other circumstances and factors. A simple example is that someone who has difficulty remembering numbers would not relish using a combination lock. Sounds stupid, but not to the person actually involved. Also, if the safe is in a not very well lit area then it may be difficult to see the dial clearly enough, and it can be most frustrating if you have to try several times to get the combination *'spot on'*. Similarly, there are people who do not want to carry keys with them regularly, and they may well find a keylock inconvenient. You should ascertain from your client his preferences, and his reasons as some may be misfounded.

Regarding the actual security value of the two methods, assuming you are dealing with locks of comparative quality I do not think there is much to choose between them.

One point in favour of combination locks is that the combination can be changed fairly easily if, for example, a staff member has been sacked and there is a fear of retribution being sought. Keylocks can be changed, but it is more difficult and more expensive.

There are, of course, safes with both types of lock for added security, or two keylocks or two combination locks, all for added security. Ideally, no person should be in charge of the key and also know the combination, or have both keys or know both combinations, thus increasing the security still further and, if this is not practicable, as few people as possible should have both modes of access.

Key security is just as important as the type of lock involved. There is little point in having a good safe, with good locks, and then leaving the keys lying around. I feel that a great number of surveyors, when making enquiries in this connection, concern themselves only with what happens to the keys when the business is closed. This is, of course, very important, but what happens to the keys during the day is also important. Any authorised safe keyholder should *never* let the key go out of his possession; if his key is needed to open the safe then so is he. In my opinion keys in a jacket on a coatstand are not in the keyholder's possession, nor when lying on a desk or in a drawer. Does he always remember to take them with him when going to the coffee machine or toilet? I doubt it. I fully accept that some keys are awkwardly shaped, but having to keep them on your person is part of the responsibility of being a keyholder. If someone cannot accept the drawbacks they shouldn't accept the responsibility. One possible way around the problem is to leave the keys in a locked drawer and take the only key to the drawer around with you, *but* this is for daytime only.

I have often found the safe key on a key-ring with a great number of other keys for cupboards, doors, garages etc., and these keys float around the premises completely out of anyone's control, free for unscrupulous hands to make *'imprints'* etc.

When business ceases at the end of the day, all safe keys must be removed from the premises and I don't care how inconvenient this may be. To do otherwise is complete folly as, sooner or later, someone will find out where they are left. It is quite amazing how many occasions you will find the safe religiously locked, then the keys left in a desk drawer, locked or otherwise. In effect, the client has paid several hundreds, maybe running into thousands, of pounds for a safe, but the actual security ends up being a timber desk with weak lock (if used). If anyone can see any sense in that I would be pleased to hear from them. Attempts at *'hiding keys'* are equally misguided. Anyone breaking in at a weekend or over a holiday period has ample time to search literally everywhere to find the hiding place. Removal from the premises is the only answer, so don't be persuaded otherwise.

Combinations for locks must equally be treated with care. You may think that because there is nothing physical, like a key, there is no problem; not so! Many people are reluctant to trust their own memory so they have the number written down somewhere. Indeed this action can be quite sensible, e.g. if there is only one *'keyholder',* what happens if he/she dies suddenly; no one can get into the safe without great cost and probably damage to the safe. The main concern is what is done with the piece of paper with the combination on it. I have seen it stuck onto the safe door, onto the wall above the safe and other such stupid places. Like keys, the combination must not be left lying around during the day and must be removed from the premises at night.

I did hear of one security conscious keyholder who kept his copy of the combination safely locked in the safe. — Good thinking! When these safes leave the manufacturer's premises they have a very simple combination, and if this is not changed it is probably known to every burglar in the country. Make sure your client has had this changed to his own personal code.

All of the foregoing comments have been aimed at the safe in commercial premises, but the majority of the comments apply also to domestic premises. Safe keys should never be left in the house when it is unoccupied, even for short shopping trips. Burglars don't take long to ransack the premises. One point often found is that the combination is based upon the telephone number of the premises in which the safe is situated. As a phone, displaying the number, is usually close to hand, it might not take the burglar too long to work out the combination. The Insured should use some imagination in deciding the figures most suitable to himself or his business.

The most suitable type of safe for any particular risk is, to a large extent, dependant upon the actual value of the property at risk. Individual Insurers have their own limits for cash & valuables appropriate to each safe, and in most cases where the value is high only a free standing safe will be acceptable. Most wall safe limits are fairly small, underfloor safe limits are greater and free standing safes have the complete range from low value to high value. In addition to the value of goods involved you must consider the volume of the goods, together with any packaging. Within each security grading some manufacturers produce differing sizes of safe, further indicating that size and strength are not the same thing. Business expansion is another consideration, there being little point in having a safe *'up to the limit',* if in a short period it is obvious the limit is going to be exceeded. Whilst this may be fairly obvious, it is not an easy problem to solve, especially if the business concerned is a new venture and the expansion rate is something of an unknown quantity.

The load bearing capacity of the floor must be considered. If an *'ideal'* safe to hold all of the goods involved is going to be too heavy for the floor, it may be necessary to *'split the risk'* and have two safes of lesser value, some distance apart, to spread the weight. Incidentally, some people consider this 'splitting' to be an advantage from a security aspect, regardless of floor considerations. The theory is that it may take longer to overcome two lesser safes than one stronger safe; consequently, if the burglar gives up after one safe has been overcome it is better to lose half the goods than risk the total. As far as I am aware this is an unproven theory with a certain amount of logic, but it is up to you, or your bosses, whether it is a theory to which you subscribe.

The type of floor or wall will influence the safe choice. There is little point in having an underfloor safe in an upper timber floor (assuming it is practicable — which is doubtful), nor is it sensible to install a wall safe in a weak wall, or even in a standard (11" cavity) perimeter wall if the outside of the wall is easily accessible. Bolting a free standing safe to a timber floor may not be much use if the floorboards can easily be cut and the bolting down process negated.

In my opinion one factor which should influence the choice of type of safe is often ignored. The physical abilities of the keyholder should always be considered, especially when thinking of underfloor safes. The person involved must be able, now and in the future, to get down on their hands and knees and reach anything up to 18" below floor level. Sounds easy, but not to the aged or infirm, a special consideration in domestic circumstances where there may not be able bodied assistance at hand. The arthritic finger may not have sufficient strength to turn a safe key, so a combination lock may be more appropriate. I fully accept that it is not easy to cater for all possibilities. Who can tell when illness, accident etc. are going to strike? You must bear these things in mind.

Let us assume we have decided on the type and quality of safe. The next big question is its **location**. Where there is a choice, there will always be arguments for and against each position. Should you hide the safe in the hope no-one will know it is there, or should you place it fairly openly so that any attack will be obvious and hopefully detected? Which is the correct decision must be dependant upon many factors, e.g. (a) is an attack going to be noticed? (b) if it is , is the person noticing the attack likely to do anything about it? (c) is the safe strong enough to cause considerable time delay to the attacker and so allow the police to be summoned and arrive before the intruders flee? (d) if it is an old or inferior safe, to 'display' it may be a positive invitation to potential intruders, and maybe even an indication of the general standard of security, (e) if the locking is by combination mechanism, is displaying the safe likely to disclose the combination to a hawk eyed crook? One point often missed is that a very busy shopping street during the day might well be virtually deserted after business hours, so don't be misled by what you see during business hours.

If it is patently obvious that the safe cannot be seen by passers-by, then it does not follow that siting is irrelevant, because it is not. Let us assume that the premises are above ground floor, and therefore out of general public view; it may still be the case that the public or customers have legal access during the day. The safe should not be in any place where the public have every right to be, otherwise they will not only see the safe but quite possibly what is in it.

It is not advisable to have the safe positioned against a perimeter wall (to the risk), as it is possible the safe may be attacked through that wall and your client will have no control over the security on the other side of the wall. When deciding on the position for the safe remember that to get large objects in and out you may have to open the door through 180° and not just 90°, so don't place the safe hard up against a wall on the hinge side of the door.

In domestic situations, location is equally important, although it is unlikely that the safe, or attack thereon, is going to be seen by passers by. Because of the appearance of a free-standing safe, it is unlikely that many people are going to have one in their lounge, dining room etc. More often than not they will end up in a cupboard, exactly where the burglar will look for them. Whilst it may be a little more expensive, I feel it is better to build it into some furniture in the lounge and try and make it blend with the rest of the furniture.

We have already mentioned the problems of siting wall safes, due to wall thicknesses, and this is even more difficult with many modern houses having unusual modern materials in their construction. Most of these are obvious and by simple tapping with the knuckle it is easy to detect most lightweight materials which are unsuitable. However, such tapping will not detect hollow building blocks (unless you use a 14lb. hammer and a chisel — not to be recommended). If these blocks are present and broken when making the hole for the safe, you will probably end up with a hole much larger than you wanted. Another consequence of their presence is that suitable fixing points might not be possible due to the cavities within the blocks. How do you know whether or not these blocks are present if you cannot detect them with tapping? Well, quite simply, unless you are very fortunate, you can't. Fortune might be on your side if (i) it is a new building and the plans are still available, or (ii) some other work has been attempted and these blocks discovered. However, the fact that former work has not revealed these blocks does not mean that they are not present. I know from bitter experience in my own house that some walls are part brick and part blocks and previous work might only have revealed the brickwork.

If these blocks are only revealed after the work of installing has commenced, one of two alternatives would appear to have to be adopted, viz (a) stop and rethink the whole situation, possibly resulting in that form of safe having to be abandoned, or (b) remove these hollow blocks from the area in question (remembering the adjoining area for fixings) and substitute normal bricks. Both of these alternatives could be quite costly. Builders are quite often not on your side.

Underfloor safes are becoming the most popular type of domestic safe, but because of the prevalence of fitted carpets, the number of suitable siting locations is restricted. You obviously can't have it in the middle of the floor with a fitted carpet. I mentioned earlier that in domestic premises one of the prime reasons for having a safe was for housing jewellery, usually owned by the lady of the house. Is she going to crawl about on the cellar floor? I doubt it.

There are no universally correct siting places, virtually every case is different and must be treated on its merits.

You must consider all of the facets of safe choice, type, location, etc., as to fail in any one of these may well render the safe either useless or not likely to be used.

We have not finished with the important points of safes, but this last point, i.e. installation, is the one for which, in my opinion, there should be no doubt as to the correct course of action. Wall and floor safes must be installed by professionals, *strictly* in accordance with the manufacturer's instructions. If, for any reason, some slight deviation from these instructions is essential, say for structural reasons, then these deviations should be discussed with the manufacturer before implementation. Some manufacturers actually advertise that the safe can be installed by the DIY enthusiast. I am inclined to think that if it is so easy to install, the chances are it will be just as easy to remove. Probably the most critical installation is with underfloor safes, where reinforcing rods, concrete mix and other features must be very accurate.

Free standing safes, especially the smaller lighter versions, should be bolted to the floor. If the floor is timber, normal bolting would be virtually useless as the floorboards could also be removed. There are special plates and brackets which improve the situation, but no way can it ever be as good as bolting (properly carried out) into concrete.

You may come across safes which have been encased (apart from the door) in brickwork. Initially this may appear to be a very good idea, but it raises two problems (a) if the safe is old, how old? as you probably will not be able to see its shape and design properly, and (b) how do you know whether the bricking has been carried out efficiently? looks can deceive. Is it easy to remove the bricks and be left with an old or even new safe? I can think of no way of bonding the brickwork to the safe without damaging the safe itself.

There may be instances where you consider that the safe requires **extra protection**. The usual way to achieve this is by having the safe or its immediate surroundings alarmed. This can be achieved by several means. Alarm sensors of varying kinds can be fitted to the safe itself, but it is advisable to have them fitted to the door and body, just in case the source of activation does not transfer from one to the other. There is a larger version which can be fitted over the keyway thus additionally detecting anyone trying to use a key. The entire safe can be surrounded by a wooden cabinet, the cabinet being wired overall and anchored to an adjoining wall, the door to the cabinet being contacted. The area in which the safe is situated can be protected by *'space protection'*, so that anyone going near the safe is detected before the attack can begin. Pressure mats on the floor might achieve the same end but it may be easier to avoid these if they are noticeable.

Safe recognition can be a problem, as often the manufacturer's nameplate has been removed. Current safes and those of comparatively recent make have a reference number stamped on them, usually on the door, on the top edge, or a bolt end. Different manufacturers have different places of stamping, codes etc., and the best I can do is to refer you to the *Association of Burglary Insurance Surveyors Limited* publication on safe recognition.

Much larger versions of safes are called strongrooms but I do not intend to cover these in this book as I feel they are likely to be outside the orbit of the readership. However, I do implore you not to be confused or baffled by what some clients call strongrooms, but which, most definitely in security terms, are not.

CHAPTER 17
Money Risks

I urge you to be careful of vague statements made by clients in connection with cash. That may sound sarcastic, but it most certainly is not intended to be so. Although these statements are probably made with no ulterior motive, they are often said without sufficient consideration. I, and many others, have been faced with comments like "Oh, I don't carry much cash", or "Oh, we have very little money in the house". These comments are inclined to make you think in terms of tens of pounds but, due to the lifestyle or business thinking of the people concerned, the actual amounts could be in many hundreds. After all, to a millionaire £1,500 isn't much, but I wouldn't mind having it. It is all a matter of degree and circumstances. You really have very little option but to pry and dig and obtain more specific answers. This is, quite often, not as easy as it might sound for the following reasons:— (i) In domestic circumstances you are in fact asking about very personal information, (ii) husband or wife may not be too sure about their partner's situation on this subject (not all partnerships are totally frank), (iii) cash is often transported from (a) to (b) for reasons which, although not illegal, have some dubious elements. There are many other reasons why accurate answers to questions on cash are not exactly flowing forth. I find one way of "jogging the memory" is to let slip (intentionally) maximum figures for standard insurance cover in respect of safes, cash carrying and the like. These figures are usually lower than the client imagined and can produce some interesting looks on their faces.

Another vague expression which can be totally misleading is on the lines of "Oh, I occasionally have more". When tied down to be more specific this can mean once per week on the same day per week — exactly what you do not want, a pattern or regularity. If you think about it, it is not the least bit surprising that people are less than enthusiastic about giving you such details. You, to them a complete stranger, after a fairly short time of acquaintance, are enquiring about what ready cash they have on them. Would you feel very happy about giving such information to a stranger?.

You are, in many cases, likely to get more accurate information when dealing with commercial premises, probably for the simple reason that you are not asking about "their money" but that of the business. However, even in those circumstances you will encounter "evasion", maybe (seriously) they think that the tax man will get to know something they would rather he didn't know!

A more rare occurrence, but still in existence, is the matter of foreign currency. I am not talking about the left over change from a holiday, but the money of a regular traveller on business and the like. This can be met in both domestic and commercial situations and is often overlooked by the people concerned, usually quite genuinely. Depending upon the amounts involved it might be a serious problem as there is very little difficulty in having foreign money exchanged in high street establishments.

I freely admit that asking questions about cash can be the hardest part of any survey as there can be quite justifiable reticence in making the answers. However, I see no alternative to polite, repeat polite, digging, another example of the need for a surveyor to have great tact and patience.

Now that you have, hopefully, established what the situation is regarding money on the premises, you have to make up your mind what is to be done, if anything. All money is worth worrying about, but, as with everything else, it is a matter of degree. You only have to read the papers to find out about old ladies being mugged for £5; you can hardly get smaller amounts than that. Horrendous and distasteful though that undoubtedly is, we in the security field simply cannot afford to get ourselves involved with such small amounts. The question is — where do we start?. Well, yet again I must refer you to your employer. They all work on varying figures and some may even have further variations depending upon the location etc. Wherever you do start, you must, without putting the client in the fear of death, impress upon him that the possession of any money carries with it a certain amount of risk. You know, having just written these words, it makes me shudder to think just how sick a world we live in.

If the amount of money involved is sufficient that you have to take some action, you will quite possibly find that your employer has some "guidelines" or "directions" which you are obliged to consider. These are usually in the form of steps where the security arrangements increase with the degree of risk.

Let us first of all consider "static money". Strangely enough, by that I mean money which is not on the move from one set of premises to another.

At the lowest level, at least, you might well find that you have two sets of figures with which to contend, ie one for periods when the premises are open for business and another for when they are closed. Even these divisions can be further sub-divided into (i) in a safe, and (ii) outside any safe. Whatever the restrictions are for money out of a safe, it would be well to mention these to the client as he might not otherwise be aware of the restrictions placed upon his business.

If it becomes obvious that a safe is going to be required then you have to make further enquiries as to who is going to use it etc, so that the correct safe is provided. Remember, when you are suggesting a safe that you should, especially when the client's business is a new venture, allow for increases over and above inflation. Also consider whether it would be advisable to have two safes to split up the risk.

Most of the other comments on static money really come under the heading of safes so it might be advisable to re-read chapter 16.

Although we are talking about money remaining on one set of premises, we must consider the use and movement of that money within these premises and its vulnerability to attack.

It is quite common, especially in small shops and mini-supermarkets (how is that for a contradiction in terms, but I feel that you will probably know what I mean) to have the cash register positioned at the door so that the customers can have the full run of the shop before paying for their goods on the way out, ie the last thing that they do in the shop. Now, isn't that an ideal location to assist any would-be thief who wants to make a quick robbery and get away fast?. One argument put up by clients is on the usual fatalistic basis of "if a robber wants the money, the till positioning will not deter him". For many robbers, maybe even the majority, that might well be quite correct, but I refuse to believe that it applies to every single one of them. Maybe, just maybe, the one to be deterred is the one with his eyes on your client's shop. Sure, it would mean re-organising the shop a bit, maybe even cause some inconvenience. Is that not preferable to having a gun or knife waved in front of one's face? Another point about till positioning — what happens when there is too much cash in the till?, If the excess has to be taken to the back of the shop, how far is the till from the back shop entrance?, do you have to go through a busy shop carrying the excess money?, who takes it?, how is it carried?, etc, etc.

Quite often in shops where the goods are placed on a "shelf" whilst being passed through the till area, the shelf and goods are literally touching the till. It follows, therefore, that the customer (or, could it be robber) is right next to the till drawer when it is opened. In today's criminal world is that not sheer insanity?. Do Crime Prevention Officers, Insurance Surveyors, Security Consultants, Cash Register Salesmen etc do anything to deter that ludicrous situation?. Do pigs fly?.

Cash in other commercial premises, even where there is little if any public activity causes equal, if not more, concern. If you consider factories and the like, the main time for concern is pay day. (Always bear in mind that at certain holiday times double pay is payed out, ie there is going to be twice the normal money on the premises — holiday periods are as well known to the robber as they are to the workforce). Obviously your degree of concern will be governed by the amount of cash on the premises at any one time.

Let us assume for the moment that your client is going to do all of the work entailed in making up the wages etc. You should ensure that the client's system includes the fact that all accountancy work and wage packet preparation is done well in advance of the money actually entering the building. This practise minimises the time that the money is concentrated in one place. If this is not done, the natural result is that the money is lying around, even in a safe, providing an attraction in a totally unnecessary fashion, awaiting the clerical work being completed. It is an unavoidable fact that time must be spent actually putting the cash in to the wage packets and that, depending upon the size of the workforce, can take some considerable time. Without making mistakes which later have to be rectified, the client should be encouraged to make this as speedy an operation as possible, but not at the expense of good security. Where is this packaging of the money to be carried out?. If you get involved in great detail in this connection, it could be an indication that you have somehow got in over your head, and that it is time to call upon the services of a senior colleague. You are more than likely to be involved with comparatively small amounts, but that does not mean that care

126

is not needed. On the contrary, it most certainly is needed. I will, therefore, make some basic comments which are common to all cash packaging risks, regardles of the amounts involved (i) the location of the work being undertaken must, repeat must, be out of the way of any public legitimately on the premises — even though their current visit might well be in order, their next visit might not be for such admirable reasons, especially if they obtain knowledge that they should not have. (ii) never should this work be carried out in the company of tradesmen on the premises to carry out repairs or the like. Even if it causes inconvenience, they must be asked to leave that particular location for the duration of the wage preparation. (iii) entrance and entry to the area concerned must be strictly controlled — if you have been able to walk in on the process then there is something wrong with the security. Not even other employees who have no involvement in the packaging should be able to gain access. (iv) ensure that the area of operation is not easily observable from other parts of the client's premises, or from other adjoining buildings. (v) the route for the money from the cash carrying vehicle to the cash working area should be inspected prior to the money making that journey, especially if that route contains any areas where someone could be secreting themselves, waiting to pounce. Any non-approved people should be cleared from that route during the duration of the money transfer.

One point very often overlooked is what happens to the cash after it has been packaged. The fact that the money is in packets is no form of security, yet many clients seem to think that the risk is over at that point. It may well be impracticable to have the workers come to a central point for paying out, as this could cause the interruption of work processes. If that is the case, and the money has to be taken to the workers, then equal, or even greater, security is required for that transit. I say greater as it is probable that the route will inevitably mean going through areas where seclusion etc is very easy. The carrier of the cash must, therefore, be not only accompanied, but also have someone go in front and behind as "guards". I am well aware that a lot of what I have mentioned might well sound a bit "James Bondish". Well if that is so, I do not apologise in the least. The alternative is more numerous losses, but even more important is the fact that slipshod methods inevitably puts someone's wellbeing in danger and that is not to be condoned.

Thankfully, the actual use of cash for making wage payments is decreasing as more people are persuaded to use Bank Credits and the like. However, it will be a long time before this problem disappears, if it ever does.

Something you might be able to persuade your client to consider (but only if the wageroll is large) is to have the wages made up by a security company and delivered to the premises ready for paying out. If this becomes a real possibility, I feel that a senior colleague should be called in, but you should know of this possibility, as it might be your client's answer.

Let us now turn to the actual transfer of cash from one set of premises to another, usually a Bank (but possibly a Building Society nowadays).

Once again, your employer's guidelines or rules must be referred to. The points most likely to be covered include (a) a security case or bag to be used if the amounts involved are sufficiently high, (b) the identity of, and how many people are to be involved in the transit journey — until a few years ago insurance policy wordings in this respect used to be quite specific, but now they cannot be as specific as many people would like in view of sexual discrimination legislation, (c) means of transport, by car, on foot etc, and finally, (d) use of professional security cash carrying companies. The above might well vary from area to area, or could be standardised throughout the country.

I mentioned earlier that certain employers have rules in this connection, but once again I must mention that I do not think that rules can be made for any form of security. Guidelines yes, but these should not be used as rules behind which the surveyor can hide. I would suggest that no set of rules can possibly cater for the vast variations in circumstances that prevail throughout the country. Whatever form of security is required, it will probably have to be explained to the client for two reasons, (i) it is virtually impossible to mention everything that is involved with a system unless the explanation is very lengthy, and (ii) most clients will accept restrictions and the like if they are explained to them, — not only the restrictions themselves, but also the reasoning behind them. Just put yourself in the client's shoes. If you were faced with a list of rules which you did not fully understand, would you be all that happy with having to comply. Also, if the reasoning is not fully understood, it is more likely that deviations will creep in without the significance being appreciated.

Some of these explanations might include, (a) why a security bag, which to some people advertises the fact that cash is being carried, is preferable to a carrier bag which some people genuinely believe is better due to its anonymity, (b) what the various people should be doing when it is specified that more than one person should be involved — the additional people have duties, they are not there for a chat, they should be drivers, look outs and the like. (c) a request to split the money between two or three people to reduce the target.

Other things to be considered include (i) how close can the client's staff park their car in relationship to the Bank used?, (ii) is the Bank in an area where the driver will have difficulty in remaining directly outside due to parking restrictions? If the answers reveal disturbing features, you might even have to try and persuade the client to use another branch with better conditions. (iii) What are the parking facilities at the clients premises? Can the car be brought virtually to the door? Any walking distances should be reduced to a minimum. This can be particularly difficult when dealing with a shop in a shopping mall or complex where the distance from the shop to the street is considerable. Most of these shops have rear accesses from private roads for the purpose of deliveries and the like. I have reservations about using vehicles on these roads as they are usually narrow and easy to block when a robbery is in progress. There is quite often no easy answer, and you have to make do with the best that can be arranged, but just because there are problems that is no excuse for not trying to come to the best possible solution.

One point often raised by clients is the red herring that "the area is always busy so no-one would try in these circumstances". That is a false assumption; the crowd of people can be the very confusion that the robber wants to "get lost in the crowd".

Another "solution" often quoted is the use of night safe facilities. Now I accept that there will be situations where that facility is the best that can be arranged, but I make no bones about the fact that I do not like them, and given any choice at all I would not use them. The chances of there being many people putting empty bags into these holes in the wall are slim. It follows, therefore, that anyone approaching a night safe is probably going to be carrying some cash. Granted the robber might not know how much, but he might be prepared to work on the basis that something is better than nothing. To me they are an attraction to any would be robber. Question — If an employer insists upon one of his staff using a night safe, is that contravening the "safe place of work" principle?.

Security firms will arrange for the collection of cash, and the banking thereof; is that the (not cheap) answer to your clients problem?.

Any transit of money should be as irregular as possible. A regular pattern is an absolute godsend to any robber, it makes his job an awful lot easier. Different routes, different times, different people, they all help to throw the robber off the scent. Let's not make his job any easier for him than is possible.

Having considered everything and made all of your decisions don't expect any of your client's employees to be any braver than you would be yourself. In this context dead heroes are not a good advertisement!

CHAPTER 18
Private House Surveys

In previous chapters I have been aiming primarily, but not exclusively, at commercial risks. We now concentrate on private residences.

At the beginning of this book I mentioned that, in my opinion, surveyors must have imagination and consideration. Nowhere is this more important than when dealing with private residences. During my years of surveying, I think I have found more examples of bad security design in houses than anywhere else, and I am convinced the main reason is that the specifiers did not use their imagination, and in many cases good old fashioned commonsense. These 'botch ups' are not confined to the actions of cowboys; I have seen many where so called major companies are involved, not only from an installing aspect but also from the specifying point of view, including, dare I say it, Insurers. A possible reason is that most specifiers and installers work mainly on commercial premises, and employ the same attitudes when dealing with houses. I maintain this is fundamentally and basically wrong, and it doesn't take much thought to see why. The majority of commercial security design is intended to deal with property when there is no-one present, and where those dealing with security should be fit, mentally alert and adult in attitude, although sadly not all those criteria are always present. Domestic security, however, has to deal with pets (often considered more important than anything else and not to be interfered with), children, aged people, the sick and the infirm. Also the protection must be adaptable for use both when the premises are occupied and also when empty. Most important is the fact you are dealing with a home, a place of relaxation, freedom and family togetherness, in no way comparable to the atmosphere and attitudes in commercial premises.

When dealing with commercial premises most specifiers consider the contents and their degree of attraction, the building location, type of locality, construction, openings and similar points; all very correct and proper. With a house however, although all of these points must be considered, the first essential and the basic factor is the people in the house, their habits etc. So you see that although some considerations may be virtually the same for domestic and commercial premises, the base from which you work is different and this must influence your whole thinking on the subject.

I do not apologise for labouring this point as I feel very strongly that it is the base of much, indeed the majority of, bad security in houses.

Having been strong on the attitude towards security design in houses, that is a last point on which I can be assertive or dictatorial on what is right or wrong, because every, I repeat every, house is different from its neighbours.

They may well have been built at the same time, to the same design, of the same materials, and be inhabited by people of the same class (I apologise for introducing this word, but I feel you will know what I mean), but the people may have different interests, sizes of family, attitudes to pets, physical abilities or indeed disabilities. Mr. Jones may like to *live it up* spending his money on food, wine, expensive holidays and the like, whereas Mr Brown next door is more interested in having ornaments, paintings etc. and can't be bothered with holidays. It is obvious the house contents will be vastly different and Mr. Brown's more attractive to the burglar. But what if Mrs. Jones goes out to work every day while Mrs Brown has a young baby and is at home most of the day. It makes quite a difference doesn't it. But wait a minute, Mrs. Brown's baby will in four or five years time be at school, and Mrs. Brown may go back to work, changing everything again, but will your office records show and be able to pick up that change for four years hence. I doubt it.

Yes, you are quite correct, working on the foregoing basis it is virtually impossible to assess a house risk and look into the not too distant future, yet that is exactly what a surveyor has to attempt. However, before you all resign in despair remember there are other cases where the answers, although not cast iron, are more likely to be predictable. By that I mean the country mansion with many, many, thousands of pounds worth of highly desirable contents and no near neighbours. From a domestic point of view, these examples may be considered extremes and there are so many variations in between.

Unless the burglar has prior information from some source, his first point of consideration is likely to be the general locality of the risk. Even that statement has several factors in it. Points he will be looking for include (a) potential reward from sale of goods stolen gauged from the general affluence or otherwise of the area, (b) layout of houses relative to each other i.e. overlooked, isolated, etc., (c) secluded points of access, trees, walls, detached garages etc., (d) ease of *'getaway'*, major roads, cul de sac, footpaths etc., (e) general activity or lack of it, bearing in mind this can vary tremendously depending on the time of day, (f) is it likely to be on a regular police patrol route or near a police station, which theoretically at least should mean greater than average police activity.

Having decided a particular area *'looks right'*, what is likely to influence the thief to one house as opposed to others in the immediate area? These factors too are multiple and include (a) apparent security, i.e. an alarm may put him off, (b) apparent disregard for security, e.g. many windows left open, garage door wide open displaying all the contents, (c) exceptional affluence, e.g. expensive cars in the driveway, garden swimming pool visible, (d) car going out with children at school opening time or returning at close of school, (e) lady of the house taking dog for a walk, especially if dressed for *'country walk'*, (f) the more obvious, but still valuable, tell tale signs of milk not taken in, papers sticking out of letterbox, abnormally long grass. Just because one or more of these factors are favourable to the burglar, it does not follow he will immediately *'dive in'*. Depending on the type of burglar, however, they may well influence what happens. Some may immediately *'have a go'*, others may only note the factors and check later to see what, if any, changes have been made, and, having summed up the situation, *'choose the right moment'* to *attack the premises.*

I have just referred to the *'type of burglar'*, and this comment is worth expanding upon, as it can greatly influence the type of burglary likely to occur. I am not going to try and get involved with specific statistics, but I would think that the majority of break-ins are committed by youthful *'opportunists'* who see an open window and take advantage of it. The actual amounts taken on each occasion are probably quite small, although the incident is none the less devastating to the innocent victim. Unfortunately, there are so many *'open windows'* that these opportunist thieves can make quite a healthy living from their trade.

If you go up the burglar grading list you will come across the fellow who is prepared to break door/window frames or glass, either skilfully or by brute force, to gain entry. To this burglar, locks etc. mean nothing unless the frames etc. are of exceptional quality, an unlikely situation on its own. This type of burglar is less predictable in what he will take; it may well be a lot or little. There is no real way of telling in advance.

Yet another type is the *'con man'* who talks his way into the house under some false pretence and *'cases the joint'* from both a contents and security point of view. Having gained this information he can return later, properly equipped to overcome the security and with adequate transport to remove what he wants. It is an unfortunate and distasteful fact that this type of *'con job'* is most easily carried out against the more elderly householder. With the average house the amount of *'tooling up'* required to gain access is minimal and easy to obtain.

At the top end of the burglar range is the true professional who is able and equipped to overcome even the most sophisticated forms of security. These people are highly skilled, and want large rewards for using these skills, therefore they are likely to be encountered only where the value is exceptionally high. This also is the type of risk you would expect to be heavily protected. As this book is designed for novice surveyors I feel it is unlikely you will be involved in such surveys until you have gained a fair amount of experience.

I have gone from the extremes of the opportunist to the top professional, but you can rest assured that there are many grades in between. What it does mean is that for every type of risk there is a type of burglar!

Earlier I mentioned degrees of affluence, cars etc., but following on from the immediately preceding paragraph there must be, and are, burglars working in the opposite extreme, the very poor area. Unfortunately, burglars have no conscience and the poor are just as much fair game as the wealthy. This may well appear to be a fatuous statement to make; you may well ask *'how can the poor have anything worth stealing'?* Do not be fooled by the most common argument put up, quite sincerely by many clients, viz. *'I have nothing worth stealing'.* Everyone, but everyone, has something worth stealing, even rags can be sold to rag merchants. This can be quite a difficult concept to get over to many a client, as they genuinely believe that burglars only steal from the rich. It is sad to say that the easiest people to convince are those who have suffered themselves or are very close to someone who has.

Another point of which surveyors should be aware, although it is difficult to know how they can make use of the information, is that burglars do not always steal the obvious goods available. I have known houses with furs, silver, jewellery and similar valuable *'goodies'*, but burglars have left them and taken more mundane goods such as coffee percolators, electric frying pans and the like. I can only assume that many burglars literally have *'shopping lists'* and only steal what has already been *'sold'*, presumably because they do not want to be caught with the goods on them.

So what are the problems we face, have we covered them all? Not on your life. To do so is virtually impossible, we can only hope to point you in the right direction.

To sum up, the burglar, amongst other things, will almost certainly be looking for a location which indicates adequate *'haul'*, suitable premises within that location, indication of degree of security or lack thereof, opportunity of means of access, degree of total activity and policing, regularity of unoccupancy, old and possibly timid inhabitants.

If that is what the burglar is looking for, what are we looking for? In the main the same as the burglar but, in addition, as we have legal access to the premises and we can assess the standard and degree of attraction of contents, standard of existing security, client's attitude to his belongings and to his security (although locks are present, are they used, and used properly?), business money or goods brought home. However, reverting to the beginning of this chapter you must also try and assess the people, their habits, abilities, awareness, age (including grandparents and children if present), resident house staff, pets, etc., etc.

You, the surveyor, have in a very short visit to try and assess the whole location, family, habits, contents and, having done so, depending on your employer's methods, either report back to your office or decide on the spot the standard of security required.

So far we have dealt with the general factors related to house surveying, but there are some more specific attributes which would be helpful, but which only a handful of surveyors possess. Can you recognise a genuine antique from a reproduction? I can't. Can you recognise silver from silver plate, expensive porcelain from cheap imitation? What do you know about stamp collections, works of art, jewellery etc.? The list is quite long. If you know about these things you are very lucky and an asset to your employer and the client. If you, like me, do not know about them, do not try and fool the client into thinking you do, You have little alternative but to ask the client and hope you get the truth. If you are marginally doubtful you must point out, to the client, the disadvantages of being underinsured or underestimating his values. You could suggest a proffessional valuation if the client is unsure, bearing in mind he has to pay for it, and it doesn't come cheap. If you encounter family heirlooms the chances are the true value will not be known, and valuations are the only way out. A very handy assistance for goods which are very unusual is to have them photographed because it is not always easy to adequately describe something when it is no longer to be seen, and failure to be able to do so may seriously affect any insurance loss settlement and could also hamper police enquiries.

Having assessed the nature and approximate value of the contents and the nature, attitude and abilities of the occupants, you must go around the house examining existing security devices, and in many cases these will be very minimal. Some of the devices you will find may be rather odd and have a distinctly *'home made'* appearance. This is where the surveyor's need for tact comes in. Don't jump in and say the device is useless in a blunt manner. You never know, the device may be the houseowner's *'pride and joy'*, his greatest achievement in 'DIY', or may have been recommended by the Chairperson of the local W.I. Condemnation, although quite justifiable, may cause offence and lose you a client. Many a client has to be taken by the hand and have every *'flaw'* in his existing devices politely explained. The same thing applies to the *'savage dog'* which is licking the hand of you, a perfect stranger. How do you point out that dogs have in the past been poisoned, drugged, even stolen, when Mrs. Client is showing obvious extreme affection to the dog on her lap? It is not easy. I suggest that one of the first things you do is ascertain, if you do not already know, the client's occupation and favourite hobbies. Surveyors, including myself, have in the past launched into the tremendous assets of electronic devices only to be torn to shreds by a client who knew ten times as much as the surveyor. Once you have got yourself into that unfortunate state it is virtually impossible to extricate yourself to a position of dignity. To sum up this point, don't jump in until you know all of the facts.

Let us assume that you have decided that security improvement is required. I strongly suggest you do not make your requirements known as you go around the house, room to room. If you do this you may well fall into the trap of stipulating something which circumstances discovered later completely negate. You must gain a complete picture of the premises before trying to colour in a small part. This may sound terribly obvious, but some clients may ask to have requirements stated as you go around for the first time. You must resist, giving a polite explanation.

As it is impossible to state when, and when not, to apply certain devices, I will go through them, is no special order, making comments.

Window locks (see Chapter 9) — these, although quite small and compact, are not all that cheap, and become even more expensive if they are professionally fitted. Some are not particularly attractive in appearance. So, to have a great number can be both costly and unsightly — most houses have a fair number of opening windows which are never, or very, very, seldom opened. If that is the case, why not have the client decide which are the unnecessary openings and have them permanently screwed closed. The screws can be countersunk and the screwheads covered with a filler so that there is nothing unsightly to show.

Every house must have some opening windows for health reasons, and the number required will be governed by the wishes and habits of your client, these varying from case to case, even room to room.

Are the window frames in a good enough condition to take screws and locks? If not, why fit them. It would be a waste of money. You may even have to ask for the frames to be replaced, a very costly operation, unlikely to be met with delight by the clients. Even if the frames are good enough, are they broad enough to take the lock. Most are, but you will come across some which are not, especially in the case of patio doors (sometimes considered windows). If you want to appear incompetent, the easy way is to recommend locks which are incorrect for the frames concerned. Not all locks fit all frames, especially if the latter are ornate or peculiarly shaped. You don't want the client to have to gouge holes out of his window frame to make your lock fit, do you? I presume that you do care.

Let us assume that window locks are required and the correct versions are fitted, remember to stress to the client the need to use them, even if the house is only vacated for short shopping trips. The burglar is looking for just such comings and goings. This is another reason for limiting the number of opening sections; the less there are to open the fewer there are to close or overlook. When doing surveys the most common clanger I find, being constantly dropped, is the keys being left in at least one of these locks. As they usually protrude quite a distance from the window they are easily seen by anyone going about their illegal business. As the one key usually fits many locks, access to the key can mean access to many opening sections. The usual excuse given by the client is *"it is an easy way of knowing where the key is"*. True, but not only for the correct people. Somehow, you have got to get over to the client the need to take all keys out of window locks.

Unfortunately, a lot of people have an inflated opinion of the attributes of window locks. I am not trying to degrade their use, just get them into perspective. It is not unknown for these locks to be literally forced out of the window frame with crude implements, so in many cases they will not deter a crook who uses little or no subtlety. There is a place for window locks, but do not go overboard about them.

Continuing on the subject of securing windows, one of the most problematic types is the louvre. They, like other windows, vary in size, but regardless of this the problem remains the same. The material holding the louvres in place is usually very thin, flimsy and easily bent, thereby making the removal of the glass simple. Depending upon the size of burglar it may not require many such louvres to be removed to allow access, this all being done very quiety without glass breakage. One suggestion often made is to have the individual louvres stuck to the holding frame by strong adhesive. This, if properly done, can be quite effective, but one problem can arise, *i.e.* if the glass louvre is accidentally broken it can be very difficult to remove the glass stuck in the frame in order to insert a replacement. In other words the idea can work but beware, as with many things there are, or can be, snags. As regards locking the louvres in the closed position, there are devices of varying qualities on the market, but as far as I can ascertain none are of good security quality and they still leave the glass removal problem, although they may make it slightly more difficult.

How do you stop a burglar making an entry through a window where he has either smashed the glass or managed to open the window frame? Well, unfortunately, I know of no method other than that used for commercial premises, *i.e.* bars, grilles, shutters and the like. Do you fancy having any of these in your house? I know I certainly wouldn't. I appreciate that there are locations, circumstances and certain risks where there may be no alternative, but of all the forms of protection available this must surely be the last resort for residential premises. It is true that you can obtain wrought iron grilles for such situations but, whilst they are better than standard equipment, I still think they should be used sparingly.

Which windows should you protect? Any which are abnormally vulnerable due to easy reach, seclusion, or perhaps giving direct entry to a location of high valuables. Watch out for flat roofed extensions, garden walls, balconies and the like, all potential sources of easy access. It is often thought that windows in flats are less vulnerable than those in other types of residence and this is often true, but do not be too lax in your attentions. Flats also have balconies or windows of other flats to which access may be easily obtained. Modern blocks of flats often have flat roofs, so top floor flats could be attacked therefrom.

Fanlights and rooflights should be considered in the same way as windows and treated accordingly.

Door Locks (see Chapter 5) — must be considered in the same way as you would consider commercial premises, as offices in particular have similar types of doors. This subject was considered quite fully earlier in the book and you should refer back in this connection. Unfortunately, the lax attitude with window locks also applies to door locks, especially back doors which are often partially glazed and where the inside of the door is visible from a window so the key is obvious. Regrettably, the client must once again be educated not to be so stupid. Oh! I could be more polite but, let's face it, such practises are sheer stupidity. When you do encounter keys left in locks you will probably be told something like, *'it is not normally there but I've just...'* You must decide whether or not you believe such stories — sorry, statements.

You will often encounter instances where existing locks have been, or you would like them to be, improved, and in some cases this is justifiable, but ask yourself, is there really any justification in asking for a 3 lever lock to be replaced by a 5 lever lock in a glass panelled door? I think if you refer to insurance claims files you will find that the majority of such doors are attacked brutally and do not have the locks picked or keys used. You may well be asking for unnecessary and unjustifiable expense to be incurred; not good practice. However, if there are other reasons which you think are realistic, go ahead.

Glass in doors or windows is, to the burglar, the same and should be treated in the same way as any fixed glazing.

Let us assume that, for some reason or other, the residential risk is considered too great to rely purely on physical protection, *i.e.* locks and bars — where do you go from there. It depends upon the goods creating the severe risk. If, for example, the objects concerned are items of jewellery you may be prepared to be satisfied with them being kept in a safe. Any old safe? No, it must be of a quality and rating to be satisfactory for the risk involved and in this connection you should seek the guidance of your employer as the values attributed to each safe vary from insurer to insurer or manufacturer to manufacturer. Having decided the quality of the safe required you then have to decide or choose between the models available, *i.e.* floor, wall or free standing. The factors influencing your judgement will be those mentioned in

Chapter 16 on safes. To summarise, is there a suitable wall for a wall safe? Is the insured capable of bending sufficiently to use a floor safe, and even if the answer is yes, is there a suitable floor, and a suitable location within that floor? Just because a concrete floor exists that does not necessarily make it suitable, not if it is in the basement and dressing is carried on in the first floor bedroom. The inconvenience of having the safe two floors away from the dressing area is hardly an encouragement to regular use. If all the factors are against using either of the two aforementioned types of safe you will have to consider a free standing safe and all that that implies, *i.e.* appearance (in a house), floor loading, suitable location and the other implications. It may transpire that no safe is suitable at all.

Let us further assume that a safe is not suitable or appropriate, but there is still great value requiring protection, remembering we are now talking about a risk where physical protection is not acceptable for one reason or another. It would appear that we are left with little alternative but to consider an intruder alarm. Of all the forms of protection or security being considered for a house, an alarm needs more study and thought than the rest. There is little doubt that to a family which has previously lived without an alarm in their house, the installation of such equipment is an imposition on their freedom of movement at all times. Not only are restrictions placed upon the people but their pets, and to many the latter is more unacceptable than the former. Can all of the inhabitants be trusted to abide by the restrictions placed upon them, not necessarily from a malicious point of view, but just sheer ability to cope. I have in mind aged grandparents or very young children, can they be suitably educated. Where are the valuables which concern the insurer or client? All over the house or just in one or two rooms. Can the alarm be restricted to part of the house, or must it be throughout. Weigh everything up carefully before saying what you want. To over-prescribe is, in my opinion, a greater evil than to under-prescribe. The latter may result in losses, the former will result in either (a) the alarm not being used as the occupants find they can't live with it, or (b) there will be many false alarms resulting in (i) the alarm losing its effectiveness as everyone will ignore bells ringing and (ii) the alarm as a piece of security equipment falling into disrepute and making surveyor's jobs harder than they already are. You will often come across clients who don't want to have an alarm purely because a neighbour's alarm is always ringing and nobody pays any attention to it. Could you be held responsible, even partly, for that *'bad alarm'*, by bad requirements?

Protection need not be a question of either using x or y, but could well be a combination of part of both or all of both. For example, a safe of insufficient quality for the risk concerned might be upgraded by alarming it. Once again, refer to your employer for his attitude in this respect as it may vary from others.

CHAPTER 19
Survey Reports

This Chapter deals largely with survey reports prepared by insurance surveyors, but the detail mentioned is easily adaptable to other forms of reporting requirement.

You've been out in the beautiful sunshine (oh! you poor soul, you didn't get wet, did you?), you've met the nice affable client (oh! your's wasn't a grumpy old devil was he?), you've assessed the simple risk (oh! your's didn't turn out to have unexpected problems, did it?), you've discussed your client's problems and may even have solved some of them (oh! he wasn't too busy to speak to you, was he?), and you've taken copious notes (oh! they didn't get wet and end up a soggy mess, did they?).

Now what are you going to do? Well, somehow you have got to turn all of the relevant information into a readable and understandable report. There are three main reasons for going through this process, viz (i) Other people will probably have to make decisions based upon this information; after all, you are only the employer's eyes, ears and mouth, not the whole body, (ii) you may develop rabies or swamp fever and be out of action for a while, and if there is no report your employer would have little knowledge of the risk he is covering, and (iii) should a mishap occur at that risk at a later date, there would be no knowledge as to whether or not any material change had taken place relevant to that mishap.

Bearing these reasons in mind, an immediate, not unreasonable, reaction might be that everything, but everything, must be reported. Ideally that reaction is quite correct, but you may have noticed that we do not live in an ideal world. If you were to mention everything, your report would run into volumes, take weeks to compile and days to read, and somehow I have a sneaking feeling this would not be appreciated in this cost-effective world.

Somehow, somewhere, a decision has to be made as to just what information has to be passed on. The easy answer lies in a word used two paragraphs earlier, viz "relevant", ie all relevant information must be conveyed. What is relevant will depend upon the risk involved and the individual requirements of those to whom you are reporting. As a rather exaggerated example, it is probably not relevant that the person in charge of overall security at a premises has only got one leg, but if he also takes the money to the bank it becomes very relevant.

There are certain elements of any risk which I feel must be reported, and they are:—

(A) **Construction** — obvious I know, but I have read reports where certain elements have been omitted, eg roof construction. That sounds inexcusable doesn't it, but wait a minute. After a while, looking at simple building structures becomes second nature, you literally do not think about it, it just happens — like walking, you don't have to think which foot should be moved next. It means that you have to concentrate even harder when preparing the report to ensure that these "second nature" things don't escape your attention. Construction details serve two purposes, viz they give an overall risk impression and enable the report reader to ensure that your requirements have not overlooked anything.

I cannot overstress the fact that you must remember that the report reader, unlike yourself, has not seen the risk. Vague, or easily misinterpretable, words or phrases must be avoided otherwise you are wasting everyone's time. There is little point in writing things like "Brick built with small part corrugated iron" — How small is small, 2%, 15%, 20%? I am not expecting you to take measurements and work out exact percentages, but surely you can give a reasonable estimate.

(B) **Trade details** or, in domestic cases, contents standards. Regrettably, the client's own description cannot always be relied upon. In some instances I feel that there could be deliberate deception attempts. Many an Antique Dealer has turned out to be a "junk shop". Many a boutique has turned out to have 80% leather goods, etc, Houses can have a tremendous variation in the standard of furnishings etc, and consequent attraction.

You should also mention how easily transportable the goods are. Take two very similar risks (no two are identical) with the same kind of stock. One shopkeeper, when he receives stock deliveries, takes everything out of the cartons and arranges them neatly and tidily on shelving in the shop and storage area. The other shopkeeper keeps everything that is in the store in the cartons in which it arrived, still neat and tidy. Is not one easier to steal from than the other, by virture of the fact that one has the goods already packed for the journey?. There can be many other similar points relating to the nature and attractiveness of the property at risk which should be conveyed.

(C) **Housekeeping and/or management** is to me one of the most important basic elements often ignored in respect of security, although always commented upon in respect of fire and safety. If the report is composite, then the reader will find the relevant information, but not all reports are composite. A trader derives his income from selling his goods, an office from efficiency and organisation and a manufacturer from the goods he makes. If these aspects are untidy and disorganised (yet the very lifeblood of the business) what chance is there of the security (which to many businessmen is an absolute, non revenue producing, pain in the neck) being organised and complied with?

Does the boss know what is going on in the work area?

(D) **Locality/location** has had its significance explained earlier in the book — re-read if necessary.

(E) **Requirements** must be detailed in an unambiguous manner so that they can be transmitted in writing. You should always mention if (a) you have varied any of these from what you actually told the client (there could be quite genuine reasons for so doing), and (b) whether or not you have actually conveyed them to the client at all.

Having mentioned that the above items are basic does not mean that having considered them you have finished. You most certainly have not, unless it is a most unusual risk. The other aspects will, however, vary tremendously, depending upon the risk involved. Neither I nor anyone else can tell you all that has to be conveyed. If we could it would mean that all risks are the same — they are not.

Plans can be another bone of contention. When are they needed? When are they superfluous? I maintain that many fall into the latter category (a crafty way of not having to spell superfluous for a second time), but are asked for to save some people from having to think. There are other instances where a plan can save a great deal of writing and is, therefore, to be commended.

Take an average High Street shop in a row of similar shops. There is usually a front door and display windows, plus a back door with a couple of windows close by. Somewhere between these, there will be some form of partitioning to form a rear shop. Now who needs a plan to describe that?

Take a modern Industrial Estate type unit. There will probably be a front door, a metal roller shutter and an office window. To the rear there will be a Fire Exit Door, or maybe two. Who needs a plan to describe that?

That does not mean that there will never be circumstances for either of these types of risk where a plan is quite justified; there most certainly will. There might be some little peculiarity which makes it that little bit different. If so, and you think that a plan will help, do one, but not just for the sheer hell of it.

What detail is required in a plan for security. Almost certainly not as much as is needed for a fire risk. Once again, only that which is relevant need be inserted. Do not embellish to show your artistic talents, no-one is interested. Does it really matter whether the cigarettes are on the left or right of a shop with no side openings? It might well matter that the till is at the door. If there has been cause to draw a plan, it seems sensible to indicate on it the space detectors present. I know of one surveyor, now retired, who insisted upon showing where moveable clothing rails were at the time of his visit. The fact that they could well be elsewhere the following day did not appear to matter, there was no stipulation that they be not moved.

I see no reason, except in very special cases, for any security plan to be to scale. They should be in proportion in that a square building should look square, and a rectangular building should look rectangular. If the surveyor is doing an accurate fire plan, then that should be used for the security also. Don't do a separate, simpler, security plan. In other words, don't make unnecessary work for yourself.

I think that it is generally accepted that when a "full survey report" is being compiled, ie one telling the reader a very great amount of detail, it actually takes much longer to do the report than it does to do the survey itself. Remember when thinking of the time factor for the report to include that of the typist and any other intermediary, and also the time for checking the finished product before passing it on.

Should every surveyor within the same workforce report in the same way, or if there are to be variations, why, and how should these variations be classified? On these questions there could be lengthy debate with differing viewpoints having differing points to emphasise. My own opinion is quite clear. Yes, there should be variations and these should be decided by discussion between the employer and the employees concerned, both surveyors and readers of reports. My reasoning is quite simple. It is essential that experience and talent should be fully utilised and not wasted, and it is also essential that inexperience should not lead to all reports having to conform to a "common denominator". Despite what I have said earlier, part of the "learning" in surveying is an element of "over reporting", this having the effect of ingraining into the inexperienced skull all that should be looked for in a risk. However, having had that ingraining experience completed, it is wasteful in time and energy to continue to do so. A long serving surveyor should have struck up a rapport with the readers of his reports, and they should each know the others' strengths and weaknesses, thus making an element of "reading between the lines" possible. Now all of the foregoing sounds a bit complex, and I don't disagree with that sentiment, but whoever said that security reporting was simple? I didn't. If you are going to have complete uniformity in reporting methods and standards, I can see no way this can be achieved without waste of experienced persons' time, and that, in today's economic climate, is bordering upon the criminal.

This rapport that I was talking about a short while ago has to be built up and will not take place overnight. However, it is essential that it does develop. If we assume that it has been established, what benefits can be derived from it? Well, for a start certain things need not be said, but can be taken as read. If an experienced surveyor says something like "the door is secured by an adequate mortise lock", is that not sufficient, or does he have to state that it is an XYZ lock, properly installed with the proper striking plate etc. There is, however, always a but, and here it is in the form of this rapport not being abused, or used as an excuse for sheer laziness.

The above leads on to another developing tendency, ie that of "negative reporting". Now that is just a fancy way of saying that only deficiencies are reported, and if something is not mentioned it should be taken as being satisfactory. Now this can be an admirable trend, but only if properly organised and if it does not reduce security standards. For it to be efficient there must be (i) an agreed basis for what is normal or acceptable. Different surveyors working upon different principles would inevitably end up causing chaos, and (ii) the surveyors must "know their stuff" and be totally trustworthy.

I would strongly suggest that this form of reporting is used sparingly and wisely. It should never be used by novices or by anyone whose terms of employment also involve "business production". That last comment could be taken as a slur upon the character of those who fall into that category, but it most certainly is not intended so. It is, however, a recognition of the very basic fact that these people are human, and have split responsibilities, with all of the problems that situation can bring with it.

Earlier in this book I mentioned that surveyors have to be adaptable and flexible. To many an old stager these latter suggestions on reporting methods must appear to be heresy and offend their long held principles. Well, regrettably I too will not see the under side of 50 again, but I recognise that progress must come, even though some of it will be most unpalatable, as is some so called progress in life in general. Hard luck; you have either got to live with it or be left in the rush.

Some of these comments might not appear to have any relevance to the novice surveyor but they are mentioned here to illustrate what is in store for them if they stick at it and progress to the experienced status. It might encourage them or it might put them off, but it is better that they know now rather than it be discovered later when it is too late to change their minds.

A note of very serious caution. There is another aspect to any report, apart from it being a means of communication between the surveyor and the report reader. The report is also a summary of the state of affairs at someone's premises. It contains not only the good points, but also the deficiencies in a client's organisation. If there is anything wrong with a client's security it should be mentioned in the report otherwise you are not reporting adequately. Because of these aspects you, and everyone else who handles that report, must be extremely careful what they do with it and to whom they communicate the information contained therein. If you, or anyone else, is lax with the report contents you could be the means by which the potential intruder gets the information to plan an entry. I regret to have to say that I feel that most handlers of security documents have some of the poorest security systems in the country. By systems, I am not referring to alarms and the like (although they may be an integral part), but to a general overall organisation and sense of responsibility. There is probably little that you as a surveyor can do about the attitudes of your fellow employees, or that of your employer, but there is a lot you can do about your own attitude. In this respect, think of the client's premises as your own, and treat the information as you would like information about your own property to be treated. Don't carry out a survey of your own employer's security arrangements; if you do, you will probably resign!

CHAPTER 20
Conclusion

This is the last chapter aimed at helping novice surveyors and others in a similar position. The intention was not to produce expert surveyors, merely to help in pointing out problems and pitfalls likely to be encountered in the early, formative, days of a surveying career. There are several aspects which have been omitted or only touched upon briefly as it was not thought they were appropriate studies for beginners.

Surveyors can, through experience and studying what they see, build up a knowledge of what will, or will not, be appropriate for risks they encounter. Hopefully, this book will have helped them, and will enable them to produce what I, at least, think is the most important thing from their point of view — carefully considered, sensible, constructive and cost-effective, protection requirements.

However, I do not think the job finishes there. I seriously think that it is all part and parcel of a surveyor's job to guide the client in the right direction for getting a reasonable job done at a reasonable price. I also know that many of my fellow surveyors disagree with me on this point and feel it is up to the client to find his own contacts. One of the fears is that if we point the client in any specific direction we will be left open to accusations of *'being on the take'*. This is where your own personal integrity comes in, and if you don't have any then you have no business advising clients on security.

Just try and put yourself in the position of the vast majority of your clients, e.g. the jeweller, electronic goods wholesaler, boutique owner, or plain Joe Bloggs, householder. Assuming they have no direct contacts with anyone in the security industry, a reasonable assumption I think, how on earth are they going to know whether or not what they are being *'sold'*, and remember most of the security *'consultants, surveyors, salesmen'*, call them what you like, are remunerated to a large extent on sales commission, or what is being specified is appropriate and in accordance with your wishes? If you are going to sit back and let them fend for themselves you must do one of two things, viz (a) not really care whether or not your clients money is wasted, not a very professional attitude, or (b) say what you want in writing in a very detailed specification which virtually covers every nut and bolt size and cannot be misinterpreted. To adopt the latter course takes up an awful lot of your time, and also presumes that (1) you know 100% detail of everything you want and (2) the client will understand the necessary technicalities of what you submit. You may think the latter is unnecessary as it is up to the installer to understand it, but the client must also understand if he is to know he is getting what is being requested.

I would suggest that you have a responsibility to build up an association with, and knowledge of, installers, suppliers etc. in the area in which you operate. You must assimilate a knowledge of their integrity, ability, competitiveness, soundness of operation, manner etc., etc. You may encounter a first class tradesman but find he curses continually. Whilst that may go down all right in the local engineering factory, he is not the right person for Lady Snodgrasse's house. On the other hand you may find a business which is a little more expensive but does an immaculate job with no mess, ideal for the *'big house'*, but not so essential for the local factory or workshop. What about the alarm company with very good engineers but vague or inept surveyors; you may get a good job done if you spoonfeed the surveyor. There are many companies who do a good job but feel paperwork is *'a bind'.* I know of one alarm installer who insists on specifying a *'fully protected door'.* Now, because I know him I also know what he means, but to someone who does not know him that could mean anything or nothing. I have little doubt that you, the reader, will have similar people in your area, but do you know them sufficiently to have an opinion of their worth and ability? If not, you may be discounting what could be, in practice, a good contact. As an illustration I have used an alarm installer, but there must be similar examples with other security installers.

You may ask how you are going to strike up this relationship with installers etc. in your area? Well, that is down to you — to make yourself known to them and get to know them. It may not always be easy, and may require *'after hours'* visits; so be it. If you were looking for an easy, regular job forget it, that type of thought is not a recipe for success as a surveyor. Do not confuse *'getting to know the installer'*, with *'liking the installer'.* In many cases the two may go together, on other occasions they most certainly will not. Your likes and dislikes of people are irrelevant. The client's requirements come first, although obviously dealing with someone you get on with is advantageous. Earlier I mentioned possible accusations of graft and one way to overcome this is to have more than one *'contact'* in every sphere so that you can submit three or four names to your client.

You will undoubtedly come across cases where the client wants *'his pal, who knows about these things'* to do the job for him. These cases can be the most difficult to deal with. You have to tread the very narrow path between dissuading the client from his proposed action and insulting his pal. Once again, this is where the surveyor's tact requirement comes in. You may have to dig in to problems of maintenance, spare parts, back up in case of illness etc., etc., all very tactfully of course. It is obvious therefore, that you, yourself, must be aquainted with all of the problems and pitfalls of this kind of approach to security and security products.

Whilst the above situation presents problems, it is even worse when *'the pal'* has already done his work and you go along and have to try and explain that it is not satisfactory. The problems are the same, but trying to convince a client that he has in effect wasted his money is harder than preventing him from doing so in the first place. One thing is certain, security is not cheap and cheap security is no security.

When starting out on a surveying career, it is easy to be fooled into the mistaken assumption that large firms must be good, and small firms must be inferior. Whilst such classification, in individual cases, may be correct, it certainly cannot be taken as a rule or norm. Many people argue that the bigger a company is the more difficult it is to exercise proper supervision, and inferior jobs go unnoticed. As these jobs may only form a small proportion of the total the adverse publicity arising is not severe. On the other hand, the majority of small firms rely to a large extent on personal recommendation in a fairly small locality, with the effect that adverse publicity from poor jobs can be very damaging. People also state that with larger organisations it is harder to get at someone in authority to complain and get problems sorted out, whereas smaller firms have more of the personal touch. There are, of course, converse arguments about larger companies having greater resources of staff and equipment to deal with emergencies and illness of staff. Some large businesses are great in certain localities and diabolical in others. All that the foregoing serves to illustrate is that you must find out what the situation is in your area.

Having found out the situation you cannot relax, you must keep it up to date. Certain sectors of the security industry are well known for staff moving rapidly from one company to another, so you must keep abreast of the situation.

Your employer may have *'approved installers, suppliers etc'*, which you have to abide by. If so, make sure you know who they are. Whoever compiled the list may be grateful for any information you *'pick up'*; pass it on as it may well affect your colleagues who have not yet heard the news.

Insurance and security are very much *'people businesses'*, and are also dealing with *'information'* it would not be prudent to put into writing in case it fell into the wrong hands. It is, therefore, in your own best interests to attend as many meetings of Security Societies, ABIS and the like, as you possibly can. You will find that the more you get involved, the more people you meet and the more you will learn. If your experience is anything like mine you will find these meetings are by far the greatest aid to your future career.

If you have reached this part of the book without falling asleep, thank you, but I ask you to persevere for a little longer.

At this point I have to try and exercise great self control and not let my feelings and prejudices run away with me. It is, however, inevitable that some of these prejudices and whines will show through. Throughout this book I have criticised some aspects of the Security Industry and also had some knocks at the Insurance Industry. No-one knows better than I that it is much easier to knock than to be constructive, and I bore that in mind when writing this book. If my knocking offends anyone, well then I am sorry, but I feel that it would have been quite wrong of me to point out to the potential reader the problems which will confront a surveyor and leave out the fact that there are also problems with our respective attempts to solve the security requirements of our clients. If my knocking stirs up some action, so much the better. At least I have made the potential surveyor aware that there are pitfalls to watch out for.

You have read my opinion of the facts and factors which confront a novice surveyor. The main difference confronting an experienced surveyor lies in the so called complexity of the risks involved, the values at risk, and the more complex means whereby some of the problems are solved.

Sometimes, of course, the novice comes out on the wrong end of this theory. How can a risk be classified before it has been seen? Well, unless there is some background information known, it is usually done on the basis of the values at risk, not an unreasonable basis to work from, but sometimes in practice it throws up the wrong results. It can be a lot easier to survey a £1m cigarette risk than the £5,000 tobacconist and newsagent. The larger risk is going to be *'given the works',* but drawing the correct line with the smaller risk can be terribly difficult. However, until someone comes up with a better system, we will presumably be stuck with that which operates now, faults and all. The smaller risk is often given to the novice with the feeling that his employer can more afford to live with the costs likely to be involved with any mistakes there, than could be lived with in larger cases.

I have omitted Chief Surveyors from this set up because it appears that once you have shown your expertise and great ability to perform surveys, you are then promoted to a position where you have to deal with such earth shattering problems as luncheon vouchers and car statistics and fewer and fewer surveys. I know that sort of thing happens with jobs other than surveyors, but that does not help me to understand the logic. But there you are, maybe that's why I am not in charge of the LV's.

It would not surprise me if, after reading this epistle, you feel that there are too many uncertainties, imponderables and fluctuating circumstances upon which to base a career. An awful lot depends upon your character as to whether or not you can put up with that. I have been asked often *'is a surveyors job easy, complex, difficult or what?'.* It puts most people off when I answer *'yes',* but I mean it, it depends upon each case which you encounter.

Despite the previous chapters I do not think that this is a job which requires genius brainpower to be successful. If it did I would have been out on my ear long ago. The main attributes necessary include (i) enough commonsense to be adaptable yet not weak, (ii) good eyesight and ability to see the unseeable and take in the unusual, (iii) the ability to differentiate the flannel from truth, and assess your client, (iv) ability to understand security specifications which don't always say what they mean, (v) patience to listen to irrelevant drivel from *'clients of influence who must not be offended',* and (vi) ability to accept that non surveyors do not, and never will, understand your job and always know that it is easier than it really is.

These are abilities that cannot be taught at universities or anywhere else, you either have them or you don't. There is a definite place in surveying for graduates and geniuses, ie the large chemical risk and the like, but that is not for the scope of this book.

How valuable is a surveyor to his employer?, you tell me — how long is a piece of string? The job, is to a very, very large extent, prevention of losses (not to be confused with prevention of crime), and if successful it's success is not quantifiable because the event has not happened, so you don't know how much you have saved. I, for one, am totally convinced that the average surveyor saves his employer a small fortune, but then I am ever so slightly biased. Because the vast majority of other jobs are quantifiable in terms of money (what else?), it drives most managements mad that surveyors do not fit into this pattern. That fact is not, I repeat not, an excuse to scive, if you do you will very soon be found out and rightly dealt with.

Once again I step down from my soap box, before someone sets light to it — it is not one of the sprinklered variety.

In the introduction I mentioned that insurance (as with most other professions) and that must include the surveying, is a team game, and I most sincerely believe that. However, the team goes outside the insurance company, it must include the broker and the client. On one point you can be certain, if that teamwork is going to break down, it will be on the *'urgent'* case, exactly the time when it is most important. In these cases time is against you, time to make enquiries, time to check out specifications, time to just sit back and think — sorry it is not present, an answer is wanted yesterday. That is when you will very surely find out whether you have the correct attitude. I could go on and on, but will resist the temptation. I still maintain that surveying is a good and worthwhile job.

Is it well paid? Well, that is for another book all on its own.

INDEX

ILLUSTRATIONS